63

Displacement Along the

San Andreas Fault,

California

MAP FOLDED, pg. 5

JOHN C. CROWELL
Department of Geology, University of California
Los Angeles, California

NEW YORK

1962

NUMBER 71

9180

Published by

THE GEOLOGICAL SOCIETY OF AMERICA

Printed in the United States of America by
The Waverly Press, Baltimore, Maryland

This volume is made possible
through the bequest of
Richard Alexander Fullerton Penrose, Jr.

Acknowledgments

I AM indebted to many geologists for discussions on problems concerned with the San Andreas system and, in particular, wish to record my gratitude to W. H. Corey, T. W. Dibblee, Jr., C. Durrell, M. L. Hill, T. H. McCulloh, and E. L. Winterer. Geologists who have contributed to field and laboratory studies along the part of the San Andreas system in southern California are N. L. Carter, C. E. Corbató, P. L. Ehlig, V. E. McMath, J. W. R. Walker, and D. E. Wilhelms. The manuscript has been improved by the critical comments of C. R. Allen, J. M. Christie, F. A. Donath, C. Durrell, D. V. Higgs, M. L. Hill, K. J. Hsu, J. J. Prucha, R. F. Walters, and E. L. Winterer. Field work was supported in part by the Research Committee and the Institute of Geophysics, University of California, Los Angeles. To all these persons and organizations I am very grateful.

Contents

ILLUSTRATIONS

Figures

Plate

Abstract

A POST-EARLIEST Miocene displacement of about 160 miles (260 km) on the San Andreas fault system in southern California is suggested by the occurrence of similar rocks and geologic histories in three terranes—the Tejon, Soledad, and Orocopia. These three terranes are interpreted as parts of an original east-west trending belt now displaced with right slip of about 130 miles (210 km) on the San Andreas fault and 30 miles (50 km) on the San Gabriel fault.

Augen gneiss and blue-quartz gneiss of the amphibolite facies, intruded by a complex of gabbro, diorite, anorthosite, and syenite, and all intruded again by granitic rocks, constitute basement terranes of similar compositions and histories that are offset about 130 miles along the San Andreas fault. Other distinctive rocks on both sides of the fault include basic dikes and mafic bodies rich in ilmenite, magnetite, and apatite in the anorthosite and blue-quartz granite, quartz-bearing syenite, granophyre, and pegmatite in the syenite. Greenschist, marine Eocene strata, and Oligocene nonmarine beds and included volcanic rocks are associated. Similar terranes, but lacking the anorthosite-syenite complex, are apparently separated by about 30 miles on the San Gabriel fault, a displacement compatible with evidence from Upper Tertiary sedimentary units that suggest later right slip of as much as 20 miles.

Post early Miocene displacement on the San Andreas fault in central California is probably about 175 miles (Hill and Dibblee, 1953). This displacement is based on the offset of unusual associations of lower Miocene volcanic works (with remarkable similarities in petrography), red beds, and marine lower Miocene and Oligocene strata. Younger and smaller displacements, although still incompletely described, appear acceptable, because they are geometrically sound and are concerned with slip and not with separation alone. Displacements of older features in California, which form the basis for statements that perhaps the San Andreas has a right slip of more than 300 miles, rest on arguments of a different order of acceptability. Available information suggests that the fault system originated in the earliest Tertiary.

Progress in the study of the major California faults, although inseparable from the complex geology along the continental margin, can be accelerated through the geometric analysis of geological ter-

1

rains. Trace slip has displaced some low-dipping, sedimentary, volcanic, and metamorphic units; intensive studies of these and other units are required to discover gross linear features, such as basin-margin lines and lines of facies change that form the basis for finding net slip.

Introduction

THE San Andreas fault, extending through California for nearly 700 miles, is a major tectonic feature of the western margin of North America. Ever since the San Francisco earthquake of 1906, its significance in tectonics has been widely and controversially discussed. Nearly a decade has passed since Hill and Dibblee (1953) suggested that its displacement might be as much as several hundred miles, but California geologists still interpret differently the geologic data and find themselves in two major groups: those who advocate strike slip of many miles (the lateralists) and those who do not (the dip-slippers).

Investigation of the San Andreas and related faults is by two major approaches. Seismologists, geodesists, and geomorphologists study it as an active and dynamic structure of the earth's crust. Geologists study, in addition, complexities added by the dimension of time—with its long and complicated history; these data come exclusively from examination of the geologic record. Unfortunately, the San Andreas system cannot be isolated as a single problem, and an understanding of it depends on knowledge of the history of all rocks along the border of the continent and all associated structures. Such studies will never be satisfactorily complete, for the project is indeed open-ended. Like all historical research it can continue indefinitely as more and more details are fitted into a comprehensive reconstruction. Broad syntheses (Menard, 1955; 1960; Moody and Hill, 1956; Carey, 1958; King, 1959; Hamilton, 1961) depend on sound regional studies, but the difficulties of investigating the tectonic history of a complex region like California have not always been fully appreciated. Perhaps an appraisal here will point out some avenues of research that may be rewarding and permit some tentative conclusions concerning the history of the San Andreas system.

NOMENCLATURE

The San Andreas *fault* is the principal break or most recent surface of rupture within the *zone* (Noble, 1926, p. 416–417; C. R. Allen, 1957a, p. 336), which is a set of roughly parallel fractures that branch and interlace in a band as much as 6 miles wide. Many of the faults

3

within this zone are older than the presently active fault, but there is widespread controversy as to definition and significance. The term, *rift*, is applied to the belt of topographic features along the fault zone (Lawson and others, 1908, p. 25); it is generally a shallow trench up to several miles wide that has resulted both from erosion in shattered and weathered rocks and from the effects of Recent faulting (Sharp, 1954, p. 23). The San Andreas *system* includes subparallel major fault zones with similar characteristics, such as the San Gabriel, San Jacinto, and Hayward. The system embraces a band extending from suspected faults west of the shore line to some within the Mojave Desert. Faults striking northeastward and represented by the Big Pine and Garlock are not included.

Several terms are in use for straight extensive strike-slip faults with steeply dipping surfaces (Perry, 1935; Anderson, 1951, p. 59). *Wrench* has been revived for these faults by Anderson (p. 59), who suggests that it may have priority. The term, *flaw* (Sollas, 1904, p. 82, 120), is less associated with a dynamic image than *wrench* and perhaps comes closer to a satisfactory descriptive word. *Transcurrent* (Anderson, 1951, p. 59) implies the existence of folds or other structures truncated by the fault, but this is not the case with all strike-slip faults. The San Andreas fault, for example, over much of its course in the central Coast Ranges, is nearly parallel to other regional structures. Through misuse, the word, *lateral*, has grown to be essentially synonomous with wrench, flaw, transcurrent, and even strike slip. As originally used, the term was applied to a fault displaying a strike separation, without regard to the direction of slip (Hill, 1947). Lateral fault is, therefore, not equivalent to strike-slip fault. Recently, however, Hill (1959) has recommended a dual nomenclature to dispel such ambiguities. Lateral fault remains defined in terms of separation, but, if evidence of strike slip is obtained, the fault is described as a lateral-slip fault. The hyphenation with slip is clear, but the phrase seems to be identical in meaning to the well-established term, strike slip.

In applying either separation or slip terms to a fault, the dip of the fault plane is immaterial; a strike-slip fault, for example, can be vertical or gently dipping. The term is for use generically without regard to dip of fault surface, extent of fault, or relation to regional structure. In practice, if one or more elements of a definition do not apply, we do not know whether to use the term or not. Therefore no term is used in

Geological Society of America Special Paper 71

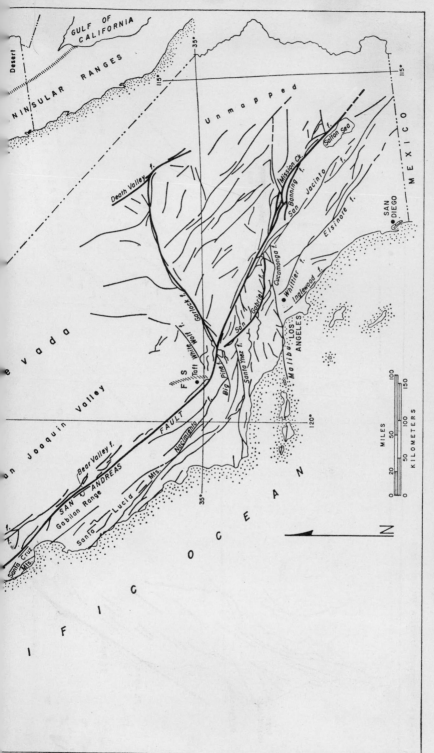

GENERALIZED FAULT MAP OF COASTAL AND SOUTHERN CALIFORNIA

Compiled and edited from selected data in Jenkins (1943), Jahns (1954), Irwin (1960), and Dibblee (1960a). Near Taft buried contact is between Franciscan (F) and Sierran (S) rocks. Principal physiographic provinces at upper right this paper for straight and extensive high-angle faults of suspected or proved strike slip; brief descriptive phrases, such as "steep strike-slip fault" and "extensive steep fault zone with strike separation" are used instead. In addition, proper names for faults, such as Pilarcitos fault, are most useful. Such names are generally unambiguous with respect to location and meaning, and they allow latitude in our understanding of their history and geometry of displacement. Kelley's suggestion (1960) to employ the phrases, right slip, left slip, right separation, and left separation, is adopted.

Extent

THE San Andreas fault zone can be traced with assurance for about 620 miles from east of the Salton Sea to the Pacific Ocean near Point Arena, about 110 miles north of San Francisco (Pl. 1). Farther northwest the submarine topography suggests that a zone of faulting, either the San Andreas zone or one parallel to it, parallels the coast to near Cape Mendocino, another 100 miles. This probably continues northwestward, marked by earthquake epicenters and submarine escarpments, for more than another 300 miles (Tocher, 1956; Shepard, 1957; Hurley, 1960), but it is not a prominent feature on the magnetic maps of Raff and Mason (1961, Fig. 1; Pl. 2). Although many maps, beginning with Lawson and others (1908, map 1), show the San Andreas fault as curving northward from Point Arena to include Point Delgada, Irwin (1960, p. 61) points out that it probably continues on northwestward without the curve.

In southern California there is also ambiguity concerning the course of the San Andreas zone (Pl. 1). The accepted San Andreas fault has not been traced as a continuous line of faulting through the San Gorgonio Pass region by C. R. Allen (1957a; C. R. Allen and others, 1960, Fig. 1). Dibblee (1960a, Pl. 7) and Woodford (1960, Fig. 1), however, show branches from it extending to the Mission Creek fault zone on the southeast. The San Jacinto fault can be followed, with conspicuous interruptions, from its juncture with the San Andreas zone into the Gulf of California where it probably joins other faults in determining Gulf topography. Faults leading from the complex San Gorgonio Pass region, such as the Banning and Mission Creek faults, are usually referred to as constituting the San Andreas fault zone in Coachella Valley (Dibblee, 1954, p. 2); this zone can be followed on the surface only to the southern end of the Salton Sea. Perhaps we should now think of the San Jacinto as the principal fault in the system southeast of its juncture with the San Andreas fault.

In summary, from near the Salton Sea the San Andreas fault zone extends northwestward for over 1000 miles, but if we consider the San Jacinto fault zone as the principal break today, it is significantly longer. Very likely the fault zone extends even farther south into the Gulf of California and farther north into the Pacific. In the past it had different courses, but the pattern of the system at various times has not yet been adequately worked out (C. R. Allen, 1957b). The San Gabriel fault, now inactive, was probably the principal strand of the system during part of the Pliocene. Other major faults, such as the Hayward, Calaveras, and Elsinore (Pl. 1), which now branch from the San Andreas or lie subparallel to it, have tectonic significances still largely unknown. In central California some arguments suggest definition of the San Andreas zone as marking the fundamental boundary between the sialic basement rocks of the Coast Ranges on the west from the terrain underlain by Franciscan on the east. This definition would include the Pilarcitos and Bear Valley faults as members of the zone.

Topographic Expession

THE San Andreas Rift is roughly parallel to the Coast Ranges, but it slices obliquely across the gross topography of southern California. Along much of its course it lies at the edge of a valley or at the base of mountains and therefore plays a role in shaping the ranges. At many places, however, the rift passes over or through a range, as west of both Tejon and Cajon passes. These passes contrast with the great eroded fault scarps, several thousand feet high, that dominate the southwest border of Antelope Valley and the southwest face of the San Bernardino Mountains. At other places, such as in the Coachella Valley, the principal fault lies several miles from the base of nearby ranges and is associated with low hills only. This varied role of the great fault appears to be one of its characteristics; it is found in all possible positions with respect to the major ranges and valleys. In fact, if California were viewed from an earth satellite, the San Andreas Rift would appear as a lineament distinctly secondary to the San Joaquin Valley, Coast Ranges, Transverse Ranges, and Los Angeles Plain.

The rift consists almost everywhere of a broad shallow trough filled with fault landforms, such as scarps, slice ridges, sag ponds, shutter ridges, and offset streams (R. Willis, 1925; Wallace, 1949, p. 792–795; Crowell, 1952b, p. 23; Sharp, 1954, p. 21). Abundant fault scarplets face either direction along the fault. Generally, they are parallel to the principal fault, but at places they lie *en echelon* or at an angle. Some scarps are the result of strike slip in irregular topography with little, if any, dip slip, so that transected hills have been moved sideways against valleys. Faulting commonly causes stream offsets which usually display right slips. Locally, however, rapid headward erosion along the principal fault, by streams which extend across the fault, has resulted in apparent left slip (Higgins, 1961, p. 60), contrary to the known direction of actual Recent slip. Apparent stream offset may also result where the spacing of subparallel ridges and canyons, which crossed the fault before displacement, is such that, after faulting, capture and headward integration result in apparent offsets. For example, the amount of right slip may be just large enough to displace a stream course over the drainage divide with its neighbor. Continued erosion after displacement will cause the stream to follow a course with a sharp left bend to join with its original neighbor. Some streams have built small fans or steep cones where their long profiles have been broken by faulting, with the formation locally of flank-fan depressions. These depressions, as well as fault sags resulting from movement between blocks and slices, are termed sag ponds where filled with water. Subsurface water, as in the desert of the Coachella Valley, locally rises to the surface by damming against the fault and supports a line of oases marking the fault course.

Historical Review

FAULTS along the line of what is now called the San Andreas fault were recognized by several geologists in the early 1890's. The first scientific article referring to the fault zone was by Lawson (1893, p. 151, Fig. 1), but Jordan (1907, p. 5) states that the first student of the fault was John C. Branner in 1891. In the San Francisco region the fault at this time was called informally the Portolá-Tomales fault (Jordan, 1907, p. 5), the Stevens Creek fault (Taber, 1907, p. 259; Derleth, 1907, Fig. 30), and the Main Coast Range fault (Derleth, 1907, p. 91), as well as the San Andreas fault. In southern California Fairbanks (1894, p. 495) first briefly described it near its intersection with the Garlock fault but did not name it; later Schuyler (1897, p. 711–713) described it and made illustrations. Geologists (Fairbanks, 1907, p. 324) traced the fault zone for some 400 miles south from San Francisco before the 1906 earthquake. The earthquake drew attention to the fault zone and rift features which had previously been overlooked extending north from San Francisco. The name, San Andreas, was employed by Lawson (1895, p. 468) but was more precisely applied in Lawson and others (1908, p. 2, 3, 25) to the fault, fault zone, fault trace, and rift.

The 1906 earthquake and the scientific work stimulated by it provided a wealth of data, but especially for seismologists and geodesists. Geologists, after exploring the course of the fault and describing its landforms (Lawson and others, 1908), could not proceed soundly without much new information. Their attention for the next forty years or so was necessarily diverted from a study of the fault itself until a substantial body of data from mapping and stratigraphic and other studies along its couse had been accumulated. Among the geologists who contributed significantly to this stage of research were Taliaferro (1941; 1942; 1943; 1948; 1951), B. L. Clark (1930), Noble (1926; 1932; 1953; 1954a; 1954b), Reed (1933), Reed and Hollister (1936); B. Willis (1938), Wilson (1943), Miller (1940), and J. E. Allen (1946). Even today the lack of information concerning the fault results largely from the lack of detailed geologic mapping and associated studies along its course.

In following the implications of the 1906 earthquake, several geologists looked for features to prove strike slip. Noble (1926) described evidence for right slip of as much as 24 miles on the San Andreas fault; displacements up to tens of miles have been advocated by Vickery (1925), Wallace (1949), and Crowell (1952a) on the San

Andreas and other faults. Hill and Dibblee (1953) first assembled evidence that the fault might have a displacement of a few hundred miles and emphasized that successively older rocks were probably displaced more and more.

Problems in the Study of the San Andreas System

STUDY of the San Andreas fault poses several difficulties. Detailed geologic maps do not exist for more than a small portion (probably about 15 per cent) of a band a few miles in breadth along the fault. Although petroleum geologists have mapped large areas of the Coast Ranges in detail, regions underlain only by Mesozoic strata and basement rocks have not received much attention. Basement terranes in southern California, even on the outskirts of metropolitan Los Angeles, are largely unknown in detail, although the distribution of principal rock types has been recorded. In the southeastern desert only reconnaissance traverses across vast areas have been made by geologists who have set down their observations.

Many of the problems concerning the San Andreas system stem from the facts that diastrophism has been continuously active in California through most of geologic time and that deposition and deformation have gone on hand in hand. Moreover, wide gaps in the record blank out understanding. Basement terranes reveal earth events of great complexity which range in age from definite Precambrian to Tertiary and include several metamorphisms, several periods of intrusion of different types, and several episodes of strong distributive movement considerably older than the faults discussed here (Alf, 1948; Hsu, 1955; Ehlig, 1958). Thick eugeosynclinal sequences (Franciscan), severely deformed but little metamorphosed, have defied stratigraphic attack. Rocks laid down since mid-Cretaceous have been intricately involved in continuing deformation and intermittent volcanism, so that unconformities abound, local stratigraphic sections are extremely thick and replete with facies changes, and correlations are generally difficult. Older rocks are deformed more than younger, so that at depth beneath unconformities, the drill commonly meets unforeseen complexities. Although major Cenozoic faults are singled out here for attention, they are actually inseparable parts of this continually deformed belt.

The dip separation at places along the San Andreas fault is considerable. North of San Bernardino, for example, the fault displays a Pleistocene and Recent scarp 5000 feet high. Whenever the fault is traced for any distance first one side and then the other stands structurally higher. Although it is possible that these differences, which at places exceed 15,000 feet, can be explained by reversals of movement or scissoring; in general, they are vertical separations only.

Within the Transverse Ranges west-trending structural and topographic swells, with intervening depressions, such as the San Bernardino-San Gabriel-Santa Susana Mountain and the Tehachapi-San Emigdio-Piru Mountain trends, appear to be largely independent of the major faults. Some are growing actively at present; geodetic surveys show a marked rising in Cajon Pass with little, if any, obvious relation to the San Andreas zone (Gilluly, 1949, p. 564). These swells are often mentioned as suggesting that strike slip on the San Andreas fault zone is not large. At many places across the fault zone, however, the basement terranes contrast sharply in character, structure, and history recorded. Present basement highs have not always stood as high in the Late Tertiary as now, since locally Plio-Pleistocene remnants lie upon broad, partly exhumed, erosion surfaces.

With regard to this contrast in older rocks, a matter of definition and interpretation arises (Hill and Dibblee, 1953, p. 449). A zone of faults several miles wide, in which individual older faults can be traced and are truncated by younger ones, may be interpreted by one geologist as a single zone of related faults that have moved at different times. Another will emphasize the age relations and consider them as belonging to distinct systems. The discussion of the Bear Valley fault (Hill and Dibblee, 1953, p. 449) illustrates these differences in viewpoint. The matter of scale also enters. Some geologists, doing painstaking work in a complex small area, have drawn conclusions only on the basis of first-hand data. Others, using generalized information or isolated observations, have made statements concerning segments of the fault many miles long.

In many areas the geologic histories and rocks in juxtaposition across the fault cannot logically be explained by dip slip alone, even by employing reversals in direction of slip through time. For example, where opposing sedimentary rocks are of the same age, they may be markedly different in facies and sources. In the region astride the San Andreas southwest of Taft, Miocene marine sediments grade eastward toward the fault zone into continental red beds, which strike into the fault (Hill and Dibblee, 1953, p. 446). Strata across the fault are marine shales of the same age. The juxtaposition of these unlike facies cannot be explained by dip slip, so strike slip is indicated; but these relations alone give no indication of the amount or direction of the displacement. Hill and Dibblee found on the east the presumed offset counterpart of the western rocks and concluded that a right slip of about 65 miles is probable.

The difficulties encountered in basement terrane, if dip slip alone is invoked, is provided by relations in the Tejon Pass area (Fig. 4) east of the intersection with the Garlock fault. The rocks north of the San Andreas fault consist of granite with large roof pendants, mainly of marble, schist, and hornfels; south of the fault they consist of quartz monzonite which has intruded amphibolitic gneiss (Crowell, 1952b). The granite and marble terrane on the north contains no bodies of quartz monzonite or gneiss like those on the south, and the quartz monzonite and gneiss terrane on the south contains none of the northern rocks. Until the ages of these rocks have been determined radiometrically, there is no way to assign age relationships.

An explanation of this contrast involving only dip slip would require faulting before the emplacement of both the granite and quartz monzonite in order to bring the gneiss against limestone. This old fault would have to lie very near the present course of the San Andreas zone. The quartz monzonite and granite bodies would then need to be emplaced with their borders at the fault zone; in fact, they appear to be truncated by the fault. Such a complex historical interpretation needs independent corroboration, for not only does it bear on the orientation of slip but also on the age of the fault zone.

A search for an alternate explanation of grossly contrasting histories across the fault has led to a consideration of large strike slip. Perhaps crustal blocks with different histories have been brought to their present positions by lateral movements. The proof of such an explanation obviously lies in finding rock units and geologic features that undoubtedly correlate and that have been displaced laterally. Much of the work and much of the controversy on the San Andreas problem now hinges on this matter of correlation—on whether suspected matches predate faulting and were originally part of the same terrain.

In an appraisal of the evidence cited for displacement on the San Andreas, as for any fault, it is essential to distinguish between the geometry of separation and the geometry of slip (Crowell, 1959). The separation of planar elements, such as contacts, tabular formations, and unconformities, may be misleading, so that it is far more useful to employ the displacement of large-scale linear features that are clearly cut by the fault. Such pre-existing linear features are lines of intersection between steeply dipping contacts in the basement and unconformities above, and lines of facies change. These lines may be straight, curved, or wobbly, but where they form piercing points with the fault surface, means are provided to determine slip. An aim of this paper is to emphasize the need for the geometrical analysis of fault displacements through the search for such lines.

Much of the information on the San Andreas system provides data on separation only. The present distribution of gently dipping sedimentary or other tabular units may be due to local uplift or depression combined with erosion. Since there have probably been large components of dip slip at places along the San Andreas, as in the Gabilan and San Bernardino Mountains, high-standing blocks may have had younger rocks stripped from them. Depressed blocks may preserve tabular units which lie concealed beneath the youngest deposits, including alluvium. In such cases data from wells and exploration geophysical studies will help to reveal the geology and provide information on facies and thickness changes; this information may provide offset lines and lead to determination of slip.

Lacking data on slip, separations may be helpful where determined on vertical or steeply dipping contacts. Such relations are apt to be more common in basement rocks than in superjacent strata. If the separations are measured in many miles, they may also indicate the direction and approximate magnitude of slip (Kennedy, 1945); it is unreasonable to explain strike separations of near-vertical planes of several tens of miles by means of dip slip, as more than the total thickness of crustal rocks would be involved. Even an appeal to oblique slip, which is more common than either pure strike or dip slip, will not reduce the magnitude of the required net slip significantly. The validity of such an argument, however, depends on the certainty that the displaced parts of the separated plane were at one time continuous, that the plane was steep before displacement, and that folding in combination with the accidents of erosion and preservation has not resulted in the present map configuration.

Older rocks, especially igneous and metamorphic basement rocks, are particularly useful in investigating the existence of strike-slip displacements. Because these rocks are the oldest available and have features that pre-date the fault, displacements within them are likely to disclose total or maximum displacements. Contacts between basement units commonly dip steeply or vertically and may clearly reveal horizontal separations where displaced laterally. Younger strata with approximately horizontal contacts, on the other hand, when considered on a regional scale, reveal separations with dip slip but may not display noticeable separations with strike slip. Under these circumstances, where the displacement of a sedimentary layer is parallel to the trace of the layer on the fault plane and has been displaced for miles by *trace slip* (Reid and others, 1913, p. 170; Beckwith, 1941), there may be no separation and no obvious stratigraphic evidence of even the existence of the fault. This possibility needs far more recognition. Some widespread and flat-lying formations, though displaced by trace slip for many miles, will nevertheless display similar characteristics where juxtaposed across the fault zone. Moderately deformed tabular units that are only horizontal when viewed on a regional scale may be displaced by strike slip so that unsystematic separations arise. This type of strike slip is termed here *regional trace slip* (Figs. 1, 2). Moreover, sedimentary veneers in a tectonically active region like California are easily removed by erosion so that the record within younger rocks is lost. These are the principal reasons why the study of basement rocks is attractive in appraising strike-slip faulting on a grand scale, but they are difficult rocks to work with and are not as widely exposed in the Coast Ranges as sedimentary rocks.

Sedimentary units within the San Andreas system show that it has been active for a long time (Hill and Dibblee, 1953). Faults have demarcated basins of deposition during the Tertiary so that highlands on one side have shed debris into basins on the other. Along the San Gabriel fault, which bounds the Ridge basin on the southwest, for example, lies the Violin Breccia (Upper Miocene and Pliocene) with

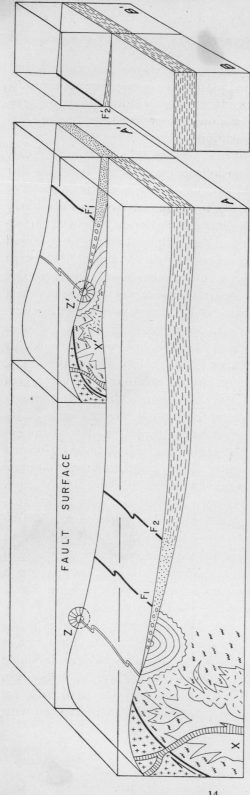

Figure 1. Regional trace slip and use of displaced geological "lines" to find strike slip

Regionally flat-lying sedimentary formation consisting of conglomerate, sandstone, and shale and lying unconformably on older rocks is displaced by pure right slip. Net slip indicated by displacement of several geologic "lines;" wedge-out line (Z–Z'), line of facies changes from conglomerate to sandstone (F_1–F_1') and from sandstone to shale (F_2–F_2'). Right slip results in trace slip primarily so that no separation at right. Cross section B–B' displays no stratigraphic evidence of major fault and structure contours in this vicinity will cross fault without deflection. Dip separation and facies and thickness contrast across fault at A–A'.

Older terranes in vicinity of X and X', schematically analogous to situation across San Andreas fault system in southern California; contain variety of rocks with same petrology, geologic history, and sequence of events recorded. Although there are numerous contacts with lines of intersection between them, the complexity of the geology and lack of data and outcrops interfere with use of these lines for finding slip. Separation of distinctive steeply dipping contacts may at times be interpreted as slip. Correlation under these circumstances will depend first upon comparison of rocks and recorded histories, and on regional knowledge that these rocks and histories are not present in intervening country, buried under other deposits, nor eroded away. With more data unique geological "lines" may be found so that slip can be established unequivocally.

14

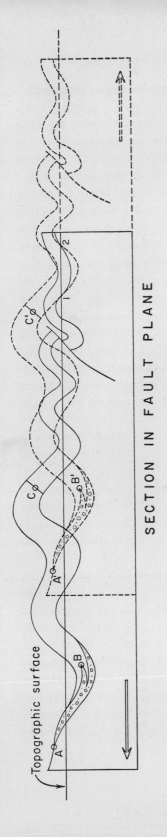

SECTION IN FAULT PLANE

Topographic surface

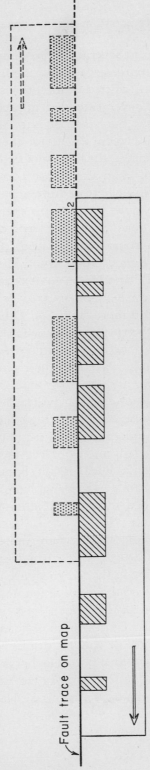

MAP ALONG FAULT

Fault trace on map

Figure 2. Regional trace slip and unsystematic separations resulting from major strike slip

At top is structure section in fault plane of hypothetical right-slip fault with vertical dip. Stratigraphic unit, folded and faulted before strike-slip faulting, displaced with right slip equal to A–A', B–B', and C–C'. Traces of contacts on the fault plane solid on near side of fault and dashed on far side. Slip defined where piercing points of three geological "lines" intersect fault plane. A and A' are piercing points of wedge-out or basin-margin line of stratigraphic unit; B and B' are piercing points of line of facies change; C and C' are piercing points of midpoint of specific isopachous line. Below is sketch map along fault. Note that separations are unsystematic although slip is constant. Some separations are to right and some to left; at two places (1, 2) contacts are traced across fault without apparent displacement. Only by intensive study of unit to find wedge-out, facies-change, and isopachous lines can slip be determined.

blocks of gneiss up to several feet in diameter that have been transported from their source area across the fault (Crowell, 1954a; 1955). Therefore, the fault existed before the sedimentary rocks, and the sedimentary units never extended appreciably beyond the fault on the source-area side. Such sedimentary units can hardly be used to work out the displacement on major faults. They are, however, invaluable in documenting the history of fault movement as they provide clues to questions of when and where portions of the fault were active in the past. In areas where sedimentary units may have been displaced from their source areas across the fault, studies of clast types, paleocurrent directions, and directions of thickening and thinning may be helpful in characterizing and locating the source area. At several places this type of information has suggested large strike slip (Crowell, 1952a; Hill and Dibblee, 1953, p. 446).

The case for successively older rocks being separated by strike-slip movements more and more (Hill and Dibblee, 1953) rests on finding displaced beds on the two sides of the fault which undoubtedly correlate. At the time these beds were laid down, however, the San Andreas fault zone presumably played a minor part in controlling the topography of the sea floor and the environment of sediment deposition. In fact, it may have been temporarily inactive. Topographic features at an angle to the San Andreas fault must have controlled the spread of sediments, and the topography in turn may have been determined by other structures. In Hill and Dibblee (1953, Fig. 2) the Upper Miocene marine-continental line of facies change meets the fault obliquely. The Pancho Rico-Santa Margarita shale was presumably deposited some distance off shore, with approximately the same trend, but extended across the fault.

The total displacement of the San Andreas zone is indicated by the slip of correlated features which pre-date the earliest faulting. But many events recorded in the old rocks are not of the same age, and all these may be displaced the same amount. To find the age of any fault that has moved intermittently for a long time, a break in the geologic record must be discovered. Rocks and geologic features successively younger than this break will be displaced less and less coming up through time. Those older than this break will be displaced approximately the same amount. Some statements concerning the antiquity of faults of the San Andreas system are based on fallacious reasoning.

Where faulted Eocene beds, for example, lie upon Cretaceous strata on one side of the fault, and pre-Cretaceous basement on the other, it has been argued that the relations require pre-Eocene faulting. This conclusion is valid only if strike slip of considerable magnitude of the Eocene rocks can be eliminated and post-Eocene slip is of such orientation and amount that additional, or pre-Eocene, faulting is required to explain the relations. Direct evidence of fault movement in the past, such as an accumulation of sedimentary breccia next to a fault scarp or debris in a stratigraphic unit characteristic of a limited source area, is rare.

A further complication arises because faults of the San Andreas system have been intermittently and recurrently active through time and have acquired their total displacements bit by bit. Belts of old rocks have been broken into blocks and moved farther and farther apart through time. During this movement the two blocks, formerly adjacent and constituting a single terrain, have been subjected to different histories so that the task of proving that they were originally adjacent becomes difficult. For example, old basement rocks northeast of the Salton Sea were complexly invaded by a variety of volcanic intrusion in the late Cenozoic. The host rocks, however, unaffected by volcanism, were probably displaced about 130 miles to the northwest from their correlatives on the other side of the San Andreas zone. The episodes of volcanism have affected the southeastern block only, obscuring many of the features helpful in correlation. The structural history of separated crustal blocks, originally united, may also diverge. Blocks have been moved into tectonic environments on the one hand where they have been severely deformed and on the other where deformation is slight. Such faults are therefore structural boundaries, or discontinuities, in the megafabric of the earth's crust. They have an infinite number of slip values, but these will be arranged somewhat systematically; separations are chaotic and unsystematic (Fig. 2).

Review of Displacements Described in Literature

MANY geologists have described recent stream offsets throughout the length of the San Andreas zone. Stream courses provide ideal "lines" for finding slip if the correlation of "line" segments across the fault zone is established, and headward erosion and integration in weak rocks can be eliminated as significant in forming the stream pattern. Areas of good exposures of rift features need study on large scale if the geomorphic and structural sequence of events is to be worked out. Such research, going back in time and perhaps employing Carbon 14 dating and pollen analysis, might document Recent and Late Pleistocene movements on faults within the zone and provide significant information on rates and character of movements. There are many data on present motion across the zone, both from slow creep and from earthquakes (Whitten, 1955; Steinbrugge and Zacher, 1960; Tocher, 1960; Whitten and Claire, 1960; Gibson, 1961), but the consequences of these seismologic and geodetic studies have not been extrapolated into the immediate geologic past.

Offsets of Pleistocene strata and terrace deposits range up to 10 miles (Wallace, 1949, p. 800; Noble, 1945b, p. 46; Hill and Dibblee, 1953, p. 446; D. D. Smith, 1959). In these cases the dip separation is almost nil, and trace slip has taken place. Slip has been found by matching a "line" between facies in the thin deposits with a contact in the source area between two contrasting source lithologies.

Offset of displaced Plicocene rocks has been described in several areas. Wallace (1949, p. 802) and Noble (1954b, p. 46) found that the lithology of Pliocene nonmarine beds, which occur as a long slice in the fault zone (Anaverde Formation), indicates a nearby granitic source; at present only gneiss, schist, volcanics, and older sedimentary rocks are exposed in the surrounding area. Noble (1954b, p. 46) suggests that the granitic debris came from terrane on the southwest side of the fault zone, about twenty miles to the northwest. Careful study of directional current features in the Pliocene beds and petrographic comparison of clasts with possible source areas will help in evaluating this suggestion.

Recently Higgins (1961) has analyzed the distribution of the Pliocene Merced Formation north of San Francisco and concludes that right slip

"has not exceeded 15 miles, more likely has amounted to 4–10 miles, and possibly has not exceeded 1 or 1½ miles since middle Pliocene time. During the same time, vertical movements have raised the east side about 500 feet."

He mapped several patches of Pliocene and demarcated the approximate margins of basins and the channel positions where basins must have had access to the open sea before displacement. These displaced "basin-margin lines" and "channel lines" enabled him to find slip in a region where at the outset only a dip separation of about 500 feet was noticeable. The formation has been displaced primarily by trace slip.

Post middle and late Miocene offsets are about 65 miles (Hill and Dibblee, 1953, p. 446). The contrast in facies across the fault is strong evidence of strike slip of many miles. They have used the facies change between marine and continental beds as a "line" for obtaining slip, which is appropriate on the scale considered, although the facies change is actually an irregular surface extending through many feet of beds. The displacement of the Pancho Rico–Santa Margarita Shale is dealt with as a "line" also, although it is not clear that the southern limit of the shale is the result of original deposition (a wedge-out line) or bevelling by subsequent erosion. The example needs additional description and documentation, now in part under study by G. L. Fletcher, and further work may modify the amout of 65 miles.

Hall (1960) studied the paleoecology of Late Miocene mollusks in central California and concluded that the boundaries of latitudinal ecologic provinces had been displaced between 50 and 150 miles. On the premise that winter isotherms of ocean surface waters are significant in determining the distribution of mollusk provinces, he has drawn the Late Miocene isotherms (and province boundaries) as coming into the California coast latitudinally with only a slight arching southward in a manner analogous to their pattern today. In the area just north of the present Transverse Ranges he finds a sharp contrast across the San Andreas fault, with cooler faunas (paleo-Ensenadian) in the southern San Joaquin Valley and warmer (paleo-Magdalenan) on the west. He concludes that the colder faunas on the east could not be explained by combinations of embayments, headlands, or islands, because such configurations normally increase the temperature rather than lower it. Hall's results, although perhaps not conclusive by themselves in a view of assumptions in drawing paleoecologic province boundaries and sparseness of faunas from widely spaced localities, strengthen substantially Hill and Dibblee's argument for a 65-mile displacement. His province boundaries and paleoisotherms, which can be thought of as varieties of "lines" for finding slip, are shown also with about a 65-mile offset (Hall, 1960, map 2).

In southern California, Noble (1954b, p. 44) described evidence of post Miocene displacements of at least 30 miles. In the region between Soledad and Cajon Pass, he deals with a "combination of geologic features" which include a "line" intersecting and displaced by the fault. The "line" is formed by the intersection of a steeply dipping unconformity with a younger one. The older unconformity involves complexly folded and faulted Paleocene beds (Martinez) lying on granodiorite; the younger involves upper Miocene nonmarine beds (Punchbowl), which, although mostly conglomerate and sandstone with distinctive clasts, include similar vertebrate remains, algal limestone, and lignite. Noble's map (1954b, Pl. 5) does not suggest that folding, in combination with dip slip on faults in the San Andreas zone, could account for the present rock distribution. The displacement of 30 miles, however, is all within the fault zone, and the total post-Miocene displacement may be considerably more.

In Noble's area there is little evidence that the San Andreas fault zone was active before the Miocene or perhaps the Oligocene, although the region was tectonically active previously. Paleocene strata (Martinez) are preserved along the present fault trough, but small areas of these beds are widespread in the region, and their initial distribution has not yet been worked out. Oligocene nonmarine beds and volcanics (Vasquez) do not suggest control by topography aligned with the San Andreas fault but appear to be aligned with the northeast trending structures of Soledad basin. Although the pre-Upper Miocene faults may be part of the San Andreas zone, Noble (1954b, p. 46) describes the Punchbowl fault, which he believes is displaced about 30 miles on the post-Miocene San Andreas fault. He notes, however, that basement rocks contrast sharply across the fault zone but does not suggest a match of offset parts.

Certain Oligocene–Lower Miocene rocks (Hill and Dibblee, 1953, p. 448) were perhaps displaced about 175 miles from the San Emigdio Mountains to the northern Gabilan Range. In both areas is an unusual sequence of "lower Miocene volcanics, red beds, and marine lower Miocene and Oligocene strata," which are presently being compared by W. J. M. Bazeley. The unusual associations, which display similarities down to petrographic details, apparently preclude the possibility that the sequences were deposited twice in isolated areas. Since individual units are lenticular and discontinuous, the complex cluster of planes of limited extent may, on a regional scale, intersect to form a diffuse group of "lines." Upon publication of correlation details and documentation, this slip of 175 miles may be acceptable.

The next oldest offset (Hill and Dibblee, 1953, p. 449) involves Eocene formations exposed near Taft on the east side of the fault and in the Santa Cruz Mountains on the west. In each area is a sequence of similar rocks of considerable variety. However, no geologist has yet compared both sequences and sought "lines" to establish slip; the data can be interpreted as separation only. There is no discussion of the possibility of southward extension of Eocene beds which may have been eroded from the underlying rocks, largely basement. In view of recent oil exploration, data are probably now available for a comparison, but until the Eocene beds have been studied, the proposed 225-mile post-Eocene displacement is speculative.

Hill and Dibblee (1953, p. 449) state that "the southern limit of Cretaceous strata in the Temblor Range may match with the southern limit of Cretaceous beds near Fort Ross which would indicate an offset of approximately 320 miles." If the correlation is sound and offset linear features to define slip can eventually be found, these beds appear to be involved in the same amount of displacement as the Franciscan–Sierran contact. The Cretaceous beds near Fort Ross are youngest Cretaceous and may include Paleocene or Eocene (Durham and Kirk, 1950). Therefore there is little basis for the statement, using the data of Hill and Dibblee, that the San Andreas fault originated in the Jurassic or Cretaceous, as Paleocene and older rocks all may have been displaced the same amount. Until the Cretaceous, Paleocene, and Eocene in the two areas have been adequately studied, however, such discussion carries little weight. In the San Francisco region, the Pilarcitos fault cuts Paleocene beds but does not significantly offset Lower Miocene strata (Oakeshott, 1959, p. 22); the fault forms the boundary between Franciscan terrane on the east and sialic basement on the west. Therefore, it may be part of the San Andreas zone (D. D. Smith, 1959). In short, there are no compelling data as yet to indicate that the San Andreas fault is a pre-Tertiary structure.

Evidence cited for total displacement on the San Andreas fault north of the Transverse Ranges is based on the separation of the contact between Sierran basement on the east and Franciscan rocks on the west. Hill and Dibblee (1953, p. 449) first suggested that this contact beneath the San Joaquin Valley might have been displaced from near

Taft to northwest of Point Arena, a distance of about 400 miles.[1] According to their interpretation the long northwest-extending tongue of sialic basement in the Coast Ranges, which constitutes the province of Salinia (Reed, 1933, p. 12), has been displaced from a position in line with and between the Sierra Nevada rocks on the north and those of the Peninsular Ranges on the south. The Franciscan, which consists of a thick eugeosynclinal sequence of mudstone, graywacke, sandstone, conglomerate, and intercalated, basic, volcanic rocks, includes Upper Jurassic and Lower Cretaceous rocks (Curtis and others, 1958). Although the contact of the Franciscan with the Sierran basement is deeply buried beneath the San Joaquin Valley, it is probably steep; it is not known whether it is a steep unconformity (perhaps with buttressing), an ancient fault zone, or an abrupt change in rock facies and metamorphic grade. The offset counterpart of the contact, according to their reconstruction, is also not exposed and presumably lies beneath the sea near Fort Ross.

In 1958, Curtis and others described isotopic dates from granitic rocks of California, including several from Salinia, that bear on the displacement of the San Andreas and related faults. Their data show that much of the Franciscan is older than much of the granite. On the one hand is an area of sialic basement made up mainly of Cretaceous granite; on the other is a terrane of largely older sediments, predominately unmetamorphosed although locally containing rocks of the zeolite, glaucophane schist, and eclogite metamorphic facies. Bailey (1961) interprets these facies as suggesting that parts of the Franciscan were buried to a depth of more than 50,000 feet. Within the Franciscan there is no suggestion of metamorphism from granitic intrusions at depth, the strata are not intruded by granite in this region, and the base of the group has never been recognized. The strata were therefore probably laid down largely on a simatic or oceanic floor and may only marginally have been in a situation where granite could have come up from below. Curtis and others argue that such different terrains could be brought next to each other along a high-angle fault only by strike slip of many miles. A low-angle thrust might presumably

[1] Hill and Dibblee (1953, p. 449) state that it is at least 350 miles, but their Figure 3 shows an offset of nearly 400 miles. Since the contact perhaps lies near Fort Ross and not Point Arena, the separation need not be more than 320 miles, the same as that stated by them for Cretaceous offset. King (1959, Fig. 95) shows the contact meeting the San Andreas near Fort Ross and a displacement of about 320 miles.

bring such contrasting rocks into juxtaposition by covering the gradational relations between the terrain with a thrust plate, but there is
no evidence that the San Andreas fault was ever a thrust. They also
conclude that Salinia was in line between rocks of the Sierra Nevada
and the Peninsular Range and that they have arrived at their present
position by about 350 miles of right slip on the San Andreas fault. The
Franciscan would accordingly have accumulated along a roughly
linear margin as a great apron of sediments extending oceanwards
(King, 1959, p. 171).

One reconstruction of the trend of the old continental margin in
Franciscan times would bring it southward from the San Andreas fault
near Fort Ross and approximately along the line of the Nacimiento
fault (King, 1959, Fig. 95). This problematic fault zone, which
Taliaferro (1943, p. 121) and others have questioned as a through-
going major fault, largely separates Franciscan on the west from
Salinia. It is shown on geologic maps as discontinuous and locally
vertical, but it also dips first one way and then the other (Kundert,
1955; Jennings, 1958; Jennings and Strand, 1958; Schwade and
others, 1958). If the isotopic dates of Curtis and others (1958) are
correct, it must be a fault separating younger sialic basement from
older Franciscan to the west. The granite at Santa Margarita, dated
by Curtis and others, is exposed at the surface only about 2 miles
from the nearest Franciscan outcrop and the Nacimiento zone; the
specimen dated came from the body about $3\frac{1}{2}$ miles from the fault.
By using an argument analogous to that employed for the San Andreas
fault by Curtis and others, the Nacimiento must also be a large strike-
slip fault. In extending their argument still further, under the premise
that batholithic cores of the Sierra Nevada, Coast Ranges, and Peninsular Ranges were originally in a straight line, we would conclude
that the Nacimiento fault has a left slip of as much as a few hundred
miles. The idea that the San Andreas fault could have a total right
slip of about 300 miles and the Nacimiento fault, subparallel to it and
between 15 and 40 miles away, a left slip of a similar amount is so
startling that it is at present unacceptable, and serious doubt is placed
on this kind of argument using isotopic dates.

In evaluating the suggestion of more than a 300-mile slip on the San
Andreas, we therefore face a puzzle. More careful study of the two
features, the Sierran–Franciscan contact and the likelihood of original

alignment of the Sierra Nevada-Coast Range–Peninsular Range batholithic cores, is required because these are features purported to predate the faulting. Obviously new field data are needed, and new isotopic age information, including an explanation of what geologic or thermal event is recorded by the isotopic ratios in the minerals, would be helpful. Understanding of the original depositional pattern of the Franciscan is intricately involved in the argument. Some understanding of Mesozoic fault zones (L. D. Clark, 1960) and other structures that determined the tectonic framework during Franciscan deposition is also necessary. Such studies may show that the landward boundary of the Franciscan was a major fault zone. In fact, in the past there may have been a tectonic uncoupling between the continents (sialic basement) and oceans (Franciscan) in a manner similar to that which might explain the apparent marked contrast in structure between ocean and continent off California today. Some geologists interpret magnetometer surveys as disclosing a relatively simple structure on the ocean floor but with strike-slip faults and displacements up to many hundreds of miles (Mason, 1958; Vacquier, 1959; Menard, 1960; Vaquier and others, 1961; Mason and Raff, 1961; Raff and Mason, 1961). These oceanic fracture zones strike directly into the continental margin, and although the zone can be followed on land, an unexplained reversal in direction of strike slip is suggested by the few bits of data available at present (Menard, 1960, Fig. 6). Data are badly needed on other properties of the oceanic rocks as well, and special attention must be given to age relationships between continental and oceanic structures and rocks.

Hill and Dibblee (1953), Curtis and others (1958), and King (1958; 1959) all assumed that the San Andreas fault is post-granitic in age, although Hill and Dibblee did not have isotopic ages available and considered the granitic rocks to be Jurassic rather than Cretaceous. Individual granitic plutons under this hypothesis may have been transected and displaced many miles by movement on the fault. Granitic rocks, however, are very hard to correlate since they usually lack signature characteristics; associated older rocks, such as metamorphic pendants and septa, may add useful distinctive features. A special effort should be made to test this hypothesis of over 300-hundred-mile offset by comparing the pregranitic rocks of Salinia with those across the San Andreas zone and displaced many miles to the southeast, although several faults of the system may be involved. Such rocks are widespread in the Santa Lucia Mountains but are exposed only locally farther north. In the northern Gabilan Range are numerous small pendants of marble, schist, and hornfels which need comparison with similar pendants northeast of the San Andreas fault between 200 and 350 miles to the southeast. Basement terranes in southern California, however, appear to be displaced less than 200 miles, but other faults may have taken up some of the displacement.

Probable Displaced Terrane in Southern California

GENERAL STATEMENT

SEVERAL years ago the writer began the study of the Tejon Pass region in order to understand more fully the relations between the San Andreas, Garlock, Liebre, and San Gabriel faults (Crowell, 1950; 1952a; 1952b; 1954a; 1954b). Opposing terrains across the San Andreas fault are composed of different rocks and have very different geologic histories. As the juxtaposition of these rocks was not satisfactorily explained by dip slip alone, an explanation through strike slip was investigated. Under the assumption of right slip, a search was made for the counterparts of distinctive rocks now exposed on the south but displaced at an unknown distance toward the southeast. Published data were examined and reconnaissance undertaken for about 320 miles toward the southeast. Although the problem turned out to be too complicated for such a simple approach, several probable correlations have been discovered.

The first distinctive rocks found during this reconnaissance that might correlate with those south of the fault were anorthosite and related rocks in the Mecca Hills north of the Salton Sea (Fig. 3). Although these rock types are not known from the basement terrane of the Tejon region, they are widespread in the San Gabriel Mountains. The question immediately arose whether they were part of a new and unrelated body, or whether they had been sliced from the large San Gabriel mass and displaced 130 miles or so by right slip on the San Andreas fault zone. Additional reconnaissance revealed

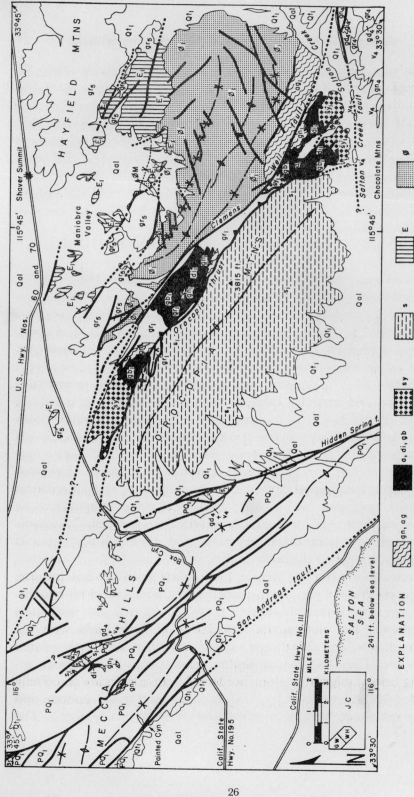

Figure 3. Orocopia region, southeastern California
data modified from unpublished mapping by Hays (WH) (1957), Ware (GW) (1958), Crowell (JC). Symbols explained in text.

On insert rectangle at lower left,

26

syenite, augen gneiss, marine Eocene strata, red beds with volcanics, and other rock types known in the San Gabriel–Soledad or the Tejon regions. Study of the San Gabriel fault at about the same time (Crowell, 1952a; 1954b) suggested that its relationship to the San Andreas fault needed to be appraised as well. The discoveries pointed to the necessity for additional mapping in three large areas: the western Tejon region, the eastern Soledad region, and the Orocopia Mountains. These have now largely been mapped, and the project has progressed far enough to present some results beyond the preliminary statements already published (Crowell, 1960).

OROCOPIA REGION

In the Orocopia Mountains and the nearby Mecca Hills (Fig. 3) the oldest rocks (probably Precambrian) consist of quartz-rich to hornblende- and biotite-rich gneiss (Fig. 3, gn_1) of the amphibolite facies that has been at least twice intruded, partly migmatized, and metamorphosed since the original metamorphism. The first intrusion consists of an anorthosite-syenite complex which includes gabbro (gb_1) and diorite (di_1), a dappled rock transitional between diorite and anorthosite, and irregular masses of anorthosite (a_1) up to a mile in breadth. Plagioclase in the anorthosite ranges in composition from An_{28} to An_{45}. Some hornblende crystals contain relicts of augite; ovoid aggregates of intergrown magnetite, serpentine, talc, and biotite suggest former olivine. Irregular mafic bodies up to a hundred feet or so across occur locally and are composed of ilmenite and titaniferous magnetite with abundant apatite. These mafic masses appear to be late segregations within the gabbro, diorite, or anorthosite. Schistose and granoblastic basic dikes, lenticular and discontinuous, crosscut these rocks, including the mafic bodies.

Syenite, quartz-bearing syenite, blue-quartz granite, alkali granite, blue-quartz granophyre, and pegmatite, all characterized by two distinct types of microperthite (Figs. 3, 6, sy_1), intergrade with the diorite and gabbro. The close spatial association of these rocks with the gabbro, diorite, and anorthosite suggests that they are closely related genetically. They also display similar relationships to the gneiss, including belts of migmatite along borders. All these rocks are complexly intruded and migmatized by rocks of the second major episode and consist mainly of alaskite as dikes and irregular masses (gr_1). The alaskite ranges in composition from microcline granite to quartz diorite, although quartz monzonite is most common. "Double migmatites," where the belt of migmatites between the anorthosite-syenite mass and gneiss meets the belt around the larger alaskite bodies, are especially complex.

On the northeast the Clemens Well fault bounds the wedge in which these distinctive rocks occur and is a high-angle zone with a broad belt of crushed rock. The fault on the southwest, the Orocopia thrust, is a folded thrust rooting to the northeast. The rocks within the fault wedge are badly crushed and deformed and probably constitute a giant slice in the San Andreas fault system about 16 miles long and up to 3 miles wide. The displacement of the Orocopia thrust is unknown, but the Clemens Well fault zone contains slivers of Oligocene sedimentary and volcanic rocks with small right separations. It is probably a right-slip fault with unknown but relatively small displacement, because clast types in the top of the Oligocene section were derived from the anorthosite-syenite complex across the fault on the southwest.

Northeast of the wedge of gneiss, anorthosite-syenite complex, and alaskite, the basement on the north consists of massive buff granite (gr_5) with inclusions of dark gneiss (Fig. 6, gn_5). This terrane is overlain unconformably by about 4800 feet of the Middle Eocene Maniobra Formation (E_1), consisting of marine sandstone, siltstone, conglomerate, and breccia (Crowell and Susuki, 1958). Several localities have yielded fossil mollusks, orbitoids, and small Foraminifera. The Maniobra Formation is overlain unconformably by about 5000 feet of nonmarine conglomerate, sandstone, and siltstone $(\emptyset_1)$ that contain andesite flows and sills (Fig. 6, v_1). Within the unit are beds of tuff, claystone, siltstone, gypsum, tuffaceous sandstone, and lenses of coarse conglomerate and megabreccia. Although these beds have disclosed no fossils, their stratigraphic position suggests they are probably Oligocene (?) in age. Southeast of the Oligocene (?) strata the basement consists of augen gneiss and migmatite, with amphibolite bodies, and all cut by basic dikes.

The central and highest part of the Orocopia Mountains is underlain by albite-chlorite-sericite greenschist (s_1), named the Orocopia Schist by Miller (1944, p. 21). On the south and west the schist is faulted against basement (incompletely studied) of gneiss, granodiorite, and granite and intruded by both mafic and felsic volcanic rocks of several types (gn₄, gd₄, gr₄, v₄). Overlying these rocks in the Mecca Hills is a sequence of about 5000 feet of upper Tertiary and Quaternary conglomerate, sandstone, and mudstone (PQ₁). These strata are strongly folded and faulted, particularly along fault zones of the San Andreas system. At one place Pleistocene nonmarine strata are folded nearly isoclinally in a ½-mile-wide slice of the San Andreas zone and with nearly vertical fold axes. Upper Pleistocene and Recent terrace gravels and fanglomerates (Qt₁) are warped and folded across the Mecca Hills; Recent alluvium (Qal) is faulted and folded locally.

SOLEDAD REGION

In the eastern Soledad basin and the adjacent San Gabriel Mountains and Sierra Pelona (Fig. 4), the oldest rocks consist of gray gneiss (gn₂) of the amphibolite facies (Higgs, 1954; Jahns and Muehlberger, 1954; Oakeshott, 1958; Dibblee, 1960b; 1961). The quartzo-feldspathic gneiss includes dark amphibolite, light-colored gneiss with conspicuous bluish quartz, migmatite, and coarse gneiss with large pink augen (ag₂). These rocks are cut by dikes of gabbro and anorthosite, and grade into several large bodies of gabbro and diorite, rocks transitional between these and anorthosite, and anorthosite. About half of the complex in the region consists of anorthosite composed of andesine ranging between An_{25} and An_{45}. Ubiquitous blue-green hornblende of the gabbro and diorite is associated with biotite and relicts and alteration products of hypersthene, augite, and olivine. The common accessories are ilmenite, titaniferous magnetite, and apatite (up to 15 per cent), which commonly occur in irregular mafic bodies, and some sphene and zircon. Dark basic dikes with schistose structure and granulose texture cut across rocks of the complex but are especially conspicuous in the anorthosite. The anorthosite has been dated radiometrically as Precambrian (Neuerburg and Gottfried, 1954; Silver and others, 1960).

Syenite (sy₂), quartz-bearing syenite, blue-quartz granite, alkali granite, granophyre, and pegmatite, all regionally metamorphosed, crop out near the San Andreas fault zone in Soledad Pass. Distinctive minerals include two types of microperthite, blue quartz, hornblende, biotite, ilmenite, titaniferous magnetite, and relict augite. The syenitic rocks show gradational relations to both older gneiss and the complex

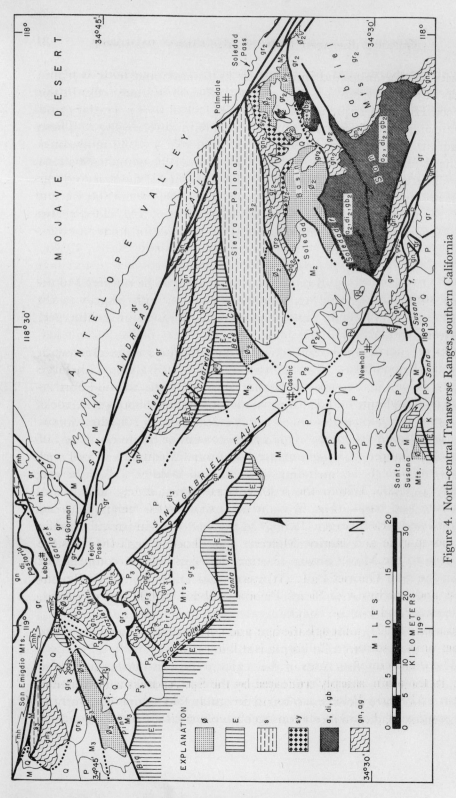

Figure 4. North-central Transverse Ranges, southern California

Compiled from published maps by Bailey and Jahns (1954), Crowell (1950; 1952b; 1954a), Dibblee (1960a, Pl. 7), Jahns and Muehlberger (1954), Kundert (1955), Oakeshott (1958), Wiese (1950), Carman (1954), Hartman (1957), Ziony (1958) and Crowell. Symbols: Cretaceous (K), Eocene (E), Oligocene (∅), Miocene (M), Pliocene (P), and Quaternary (Q). Other symbols explained in text.

of gabbro, diorite, and anorthosite; they clearly crosscut both at places. The intimate association with the gabbro, diorite, and anorthosite suggests close genetic relationship. Both of these suites, as well as the older gneisses which they intrude (gn$_2$, ag$_2$), have been complexly intruded by rocks ranging between granite and quartz diorite (gr$_2$). In the central part of the anorthosite mass is a large area intimately invaded by dikes and irregular bodies of alaskite. To the east are various granitic rocks and gneisses which have not yet been mapped and studied in detail (Fig. 4). All of the anorthosite-syenite complex lies southwest of the San Andreas fault except possibly for a few small exposures to the northeast in the Valyermo quadrangle (Noble, 1954a). Here diorite and gabbro occur as contact metamorphosed pendants in quartz monzonite, and it is unknown whether they lie northeast of the fault zone (and occupy an anomalous position with respect to the hypothesis of 130-mile slip) or lie within the zone in a fault slice (Crowell and Walker, 1962).

On the north is a large body of albite-chlorite-sericite greenschist (s$_2$), the Pelona Schist (Muehlberger and Hill, 1958), which underlies Sierra Pelona and is separated from the rocks of the Soledad Pass region by a mylonite and distributive movement zone. South and east of this zone the nonmarine Oligocene Vasquez Group ($\emptyset_2$) lies unconformably upon basement. This group consists of as much as 12,500 feet of megabreccia, conglomerate, sandstone, siltstone, and tuff with evaporite interbeds, including gypsum and borates (Muehlberger, 1958, p. 1823). Within the sediments are flows, sheets, and sills of andesite and basalt (Fig. 6, v$_2$) which exceed 4000 feet in thickness (Jahns and Muehlberger, 1954). On the west the Vasquez is overlain by nonmarine and marine Miocene and Pliocene beds (M$_2$, P$_2$) belonging to the Mint Canyon, Castaic, Towsley, and Pico formations near the San Gabriel fault (Winterer and Durham, 1958). To the west and northwest of Sierra Pelona is about 12,000 feet of marine Paleocene and Eocene conglomerate, sandstone, and mudstone (E$_2$) (Johnson, 1952), although the age and correlation of these beds with other units in southern California is still uncertain.

The dominant structures in the region trend east-northeasterly and are, in the main, sharply truncated by the San Andreas zone. Soledad basin and Sierra Pelona are broad irregular folds plunging gently to the southwest. Faults of several ages have a similar east-northeasterly but more irregular trend. As shown by coarse megabreccias, many of these were active in the Oligocene and Early Miocene but then ceased movement in the Middle Miocene; they are overlapped by Middle Miocene sedimentary formations.

TEJON REGION

South of the San Andreas fault in the Tejon Pass region, the rocks consist primarily of gray gneiss (gn_3) and migmatite of the amphibolite facies with wide areas of layered gneiss characterized by large pink feldspar augen (ag_3) (Crowell, 1950, 1952b; Carman, 1954). These rocks are complexly intruded by several granitic bodies, composed primarily of quartz monzonite and alaskite (gr_3). On the west a narrow slice of albite-chlorite-sericite greenschist (s_3) extends for about 9 miles next to the San Andreas fault. It is separated on the south from pink coarse granite and contorted gneiss by a steep fault zone with mylonite.

In the western Tejon region, and unconformably lying upon granite (gr_3) north of the Big Pine fault, although the contact is now largely faulted, are about 2100 feet of marine Middle Eocene beds (E_3) (Carman, 1954; Kirkpatrick, 1958). These strata include buff sandstone and siltstone with some conglomerate. The Eocene in turn is followed stratigraphically by several thousand feet of Oligocene conglomerate, breccia, sandstone, and siltstone $(\emptyset_3)$ with some interbeds of evaporites and borates. Associated are thick basalt flows and breccias (Fig. 6 v_3). Above these are several Miocene (M_3), Pliocene (P_3), and Quaternary (Q) nonmarine units.

In the Tejon region several major faults radiate from the vicinity where the San Andreas fault has a westward trend for a few miles. These include the Garlock, Big Pine, San Gabriel, Liebre, and Clearwater among the high-angle fault zones, and the Frazier Mountain and Pastoria thrusts, among the low-angle faults (Fig. 4). The Clearwater, Liebre, and San Gabriel faults have been overlapped by successively younger Pliocene and Pleistocene beds but no doubt continue into this structural hub at depth. The San Gabriel fault trends first beneath the overlapping Pleistocene and then beneath two plates of the folded Frazier Mountain thrust complex (which bring gneiss above overturned Pleistocene) before meeting the San Andreas fault zone near its juncture with the Big Pine fault zone (Crowell, 1950).

The Garlock fault zone (Hess, 1910; Hulin, 1925; Dibblee, 1952; Hill and Dibblee, 1953, p. 451; Muehlburger, 1954; G. I. Smith, 1962) extends eastward from the San Andreas zone for nearly 160 miles where it meets the Death Valley fault zone (Noble and Wright, 1954, Pl. 7). Like the San Andreas fault, it lies in a straight topographic sulcus which in desert areas includes fault features little modified by erosion, so that it appears to have moved recently. Stream offsets and gash fractures indicate left slip of relatively recent age (Dibblee, 1952; Hill and Dibblee, 1953, p. 451; Muehlberger, 1954). However, G. I. Smith (1960) suggested that even in the desert, where fault topography is best developed, it may not have moved significantly in the last 50,000 years or so. In the Tejon region, alluvium and several terrace levels are not displaced, so its last movement is significantly older than that on the San Andreas (Crowell, 1952b). The antiquity of the Garlock fault is unknown, although Hulin (1925, p. 64) argued that it might be as old as late Mesozoic. Hewett (1954, p. 15) suggested that it might have existed when Eocene nonmarine beds (Goler Formation) were laid down. Dibblee (1952, p. 41) states that cross-bedding in this formation suggests deposition from rivers flowing southwestward, which would be subparallel to and toward the present line of the fault. The character of the deposits required considerable local relief, presumably the result of tectonic activity, but there is yet no compelling evidence to show alignment with the present Garlock zone.

Dip separations are conspicuous along the Garlock fault, and there are some strike separations. A contact between quartz monzonite and Paleozoic metasediments might be offset left laterally about 5 miles (Hulin, 1925, p. 63), but this correlation has not been reviewed recently. G. I. Smith (1962) correlated a northwest-trending dike swarm in basement terrane across the fault with about 40 miles of left separation. Moore (1959) shows a right offset of the "quartz diorite boundary line" at the Garlock zone of about the same amount, but the significance and interpretation of the line are still unknown. Nevertheless, the Garlock is certainly a left-slip fault predominately and probably has a displacement as large as 40 miles. The time of origin is unknown, although it may be Paleocene or Eocene (possibly even Mesozoic); it may have stopped moving significantly in the late Pleistocene or early Recent.

The Big Pine fault, which intersects the San Andreas zone about 6 miles west of the Garlock fault, extends west-southwestward for about 50 miles (Hill and Dibblee, 1953, p. 451; Fisher and Dibblee, 1961). Topographically, it is nowhere as conspicuous as the San Andreas or Garlock, although a shallow furrow with some scarplets is present. Although there appear to be more streams with left offsets than right along the total course of the fault, the apparent stream offsets may owe their present pattern to headward erosion in softened rocks. The Big Pine fault has not moved as recently as the San Andreas fault, but whether its last movement has been as recent as that of the Garlock has not been proved independently. Carman (1954, p. 145) notes that several small faults of very recent age transect the Big Pine zone.

Some clue as to the age of the Big Pine fault is afforded by Eocene beds south of the present trace of the fault, which show rapid facies changes toward the northeast (Schlee, 1952; Kiessling, 1958) and little relation to the trend of the fault, although the region was tectonically active. On the other hand, Oligocene nonmarine strata with volcanics were laid down in a narrow trough aligned parallel to the fault, and the uppermost thick breccias were shed northward from an escarpment that was either the Big Pine fault scarp, or a scarp closely parallel to it (Carman, 1954, p. 88, 143). Therefore the fault probably existed in late Oligocene time, although it may have originated somewhat earlier. These breccias are clearly derived from a southern source of gneiss, augen gneiss, and granitic rocks. At present, across the Big Pine fault in the source direction, Eocene sediments are preserved, and the only known source of the proper composition likely to have been available in the Oligocene lies about 10 miles to the east. This argument, which needs further detailed work for verification, suggests left slip of between 5 and 10 miles. Since basement terranes on both sides of the Big Pine fault are very similar, left slip on the fault probably does not total much more.

Hill and Dibblee (1953, p. 452) concluded that the Big Pine fault had a probable minimum left slip of 8 miles based on the separation of several features. Offset counterparts of a major syncline and a northeast trending fault between Eocene and Miocene beds are displaced this amount. Recently Poynor (1960) re-examined this suggestion and found that the similarities in the stratigraphies, the presence of identical rhyolite intrusions, and the similarities of two offset faults provided enough data to determine a net slip of about $8\frac{1}{2}$ miles with a southwest pitch of 6°. The "lines" used by Poynor in solving this problem were those formed by the intersection of stratigraphic "horizons" with older faults. This displacement accumulated in post-Miocene time in the area between 12 and 25 miles from the San Andreas fault. In fact, northwest-trending structures were probably dominant in this region before post-Miocene displacement. If all these hypotheses are correct, the Big Pine fault may have existed in the late Oligocene (or perhaps earlier), was quiescent for most of the Miocene when the northwest structures were dominant, and then was reactivated vigorously in the late Cenozoic. A similar complex interplay between two sets of strike-slip faults has recently been described for late Miocene movements on the Malibu-Cucamonga and Whittier faults in Los Angeles (Lamar, 1961).

Hill and Dibblee (1953, p. 453) suggested that the Garlock and Big Pine faults were probably aligned in the past as one fault which has been offset about 5 or 6 miles by the latest movements on the San Andreas zone. Previous to this offset the San Andreas was presumably a straighter fault than at present, and its sharp bend in this vicinity may have been the result of shift during the time of displacement on the Garlock–Big Pine fault. According to them, the San Andreas fault was active, then the Garlock–Big Pine, and then the San Andreas again. It now seems probable that the Big Pine and perhaps the Garlock faults were active in the Oligocene at a time which either corresponded to movement on the San Andreas fault or preceded a great deal of it. If, as discussed below, the San Andreas zone has a post-Oligocene right slip of at least 160 miles, the Big Pine and Garlock obviously were not aligned in mid-Tertiary time. Although the Big Pine and Garlock faults may have been a single through-going fault during late movements, they must have been independent earlier. It is equally likely that they were independent faults during their late movements. An understanding of the relations between the Garlock, Big Pine, and San Andreas faults and whether they are parts of a conjugate shear system awaits more field work.

COMPARISON AND COMMENTS

The remarkable similarities of the rocks and geologic histories of the three regions (Orocopia, Soledad, and Tejon) raises the possibility that these distant terrains were once contiguous and have since been displaced on the San Andreas and San Gabriel faults. Figure 5 shows a west-trending belt that has perhaps been broken apart and displaced, about 130 miles on the San Andreas fault and 20–30 miles on the San Gabriel fault. This hypothesis depends on whether the match between the regions is so close that the possibility of the coincident reoccurrence of like events and rocks at great distance is unacceptably remote. Enough is now known about the terrain between, with the possible exception of the gabbro and diorite exposures in the Valyermo quadrangle (Noble, 1954a), to be fairly certain that blocks with similar histories and rocks have not been overlooked nor concealed by younger deposits. The rocks and histories are compared below, but displaced geologic "lines" which correlate unequivocally have not yet been discovered.

The older basement rocks of the Orocopia and Soledad areas are similar (Fig. 6). In each, gneiss (gn_1, gn_2), augen gneiss (ag_1, ag_2), gabbro (gb_1, gb_2), diorite (di_1, di_2), anorthosite (a_1, a_2), syenite (sy_1, sy_2), quartz-bearing syenite, blue-quartz granite, alkali granite,

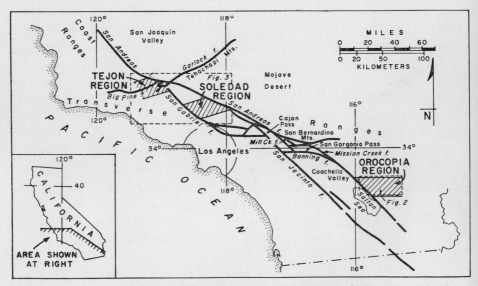

Figure 5. Tejon, Soledad, and Orocopia terranes in southern California; probably displaced by San Andreas fault system.
Only few faults of system shown

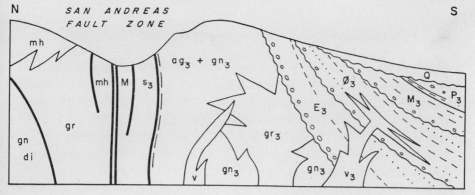

TEJON REGION

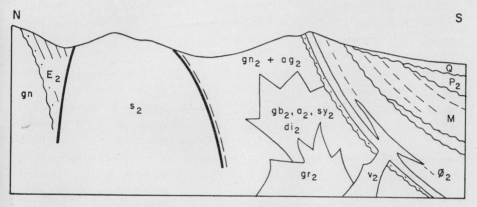

SOLEDAD REGION

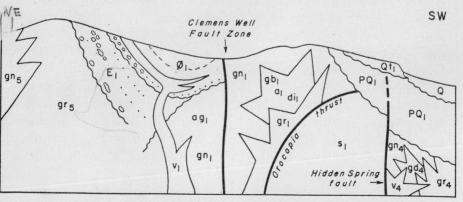

OROCOPIA REGION

Figure 6. Diagrammatic geologic sections showing rock relations in Tejon, Soledad, and Orocopia regions

Drawings schematic and not to scale. Symbols in text and on Figures 3 and 4

granophyre, pegmatite, and other rocks are nearly identical petrographically. In both areas these older rocks are complexly intruded
by granitic rocks (gr_1, gr_2), and similar migmatites have resulted. The
granitic rocks, including rocks ranging from alaskite to quartz diorite,
lack distinctive megascopic character so that intensive studies must
still be undertaken to establish this correlation. Radiometric age
dating may be helpful in solving this problem. The Pelona Schist
(s_2) is nearly identical to the Orocopia Schist (s_1), (Hill and Dibblee,
1953, p. 450). These rocks have undergone similar metamorphic
events and originated as similar sediments with perhaps included
volcanics. Both areas consist of old gneiss intruded by a differentiated
complex of anorthosite-syenite, in turn intruded—perhaps twice—by
granitic rocks and associated with greenschist.

The younger rocks of the Orocopia and Soledad regions are also
similar, although middle Eocene beds are not preserved or exposed
in the eastern Soledad area. The Paleocene and Eocene strata northwest of Sierra Pelona (E_2) are not known to correlate with the Orocopia Eocene, but detailed studies have not yet been made. Beds of
the same age are included in both sections, however. The Orocopia
and Soledad regions contain like sequences of Oligocene rocks ($\emptyset_1$,
$\emptyset_2$) that include associated volcanic rocks (Fig. 6, v_1, v_2) and related
sediments, but facies changes are so marked that unit-by-unit correlation will never be possible. There is also a considerable difference
in the occurrence of some of the volcanic rocks, which may not be
entirely of the same composition. In fact, these Oligocene rocks may
have accumulated in separate basins so that the similar lithologies
reflect only similar climates and similar nearby source rocks. Volcanic
dikes and feeders have not been reported from intervening areas,
however, nor from areas across the San Andreas from their present
occurrences, so it is unlikely that erosion has stripped away similar
sequences. Further study of the Oligocene volcanic rocks is essential.
Strata younger than Oligocene were probably laid down in basins,
in part defined by the large faults, after the faults had acquired
considerable displacement; the tectonic histories of these basins have
not yet been worked out.

Although our knowledge is incomplete, the suggested displacement
of 130 miles on the San Andreas fault between the Soledad and
Orocopia regions apparently must have accumulated since the early

Miocene. The youngest rocks incorporated in the two similar terrains are of this age or slightly older. Such a displacement obviously required a through-going fault in the complex San Gorgonio Pass region, although the Recent San Andreas fault abuts against the Banning fault (C. R. Allen, 1957a, p. 337). The hypothesis implies that slivers within the fault zone between the two distant areas might include rock types from the two terrains. Perhaps the distribution of Oligocene and Miocene strata in the area described by Noble (1954b) may be accounted for in this way. According to this suggestion, the displacements of up to 30 miles may be interpreted as partial displacements within the fault zone only. Slices of basement types between the Soledad and Orocopia region have not been studied systematically, although a few which may be intermediate "horses" have been recognized. One of these is a slice of Pelona–Orocopia type schist (C. R. Allen, 1957a, p. 321) north of San Gorgonio Pass, but the separation of greenschists along and within the fault zone has questionable significance with regard to slip until prefaulting distribution is better understood.

Between the Soledad and Tejon regions lies the San Gabriel fault, which has a total right-slip component of between 20 and 30 miles, although the dip-slip component at the northwest may be as much as 15,000 feet. The present distribution of two separate units of coarse clastic sediments with reference to their probable source areas suggests a right slip of about 20 miles, acquired by nearly continuous movement throughout the Pliocene (Crowell, 1952a; 1954b). Southwest of the fault and extending into the fault zone are Upper Miocene coarse conglomerates with clasts of gabbro, diorite, anorthosite, and related rocks, as well as gneiss and some granite. These were derived from across the fault to the northeast, as shown by directions of thinning and sedimentary structures; in that area at present are sedimentary rocks older than the conglomerate. Source area and derived conglomerates match with right slip of about 20 miles. In addition, the Violin Breccia, which lies along the San Gabriel fault on its northeastern side, is a remarkable unit more than 27,000 feet thick stratigraphically, although it extends along the strike for no more than 6000 feet (Crowell, 1955). It accumulated as talus and steep fan deposits during the span between late Miocene and early Pliocene and required nearly continuous rejuvenation of the San Gabriel fault scarp. The clast types predominate in gneiss and match with a source area southwest of the fault in the Tejon region. More than 15 miles of right slip is required to account for the present position of the older elements of the breccia, although the younger parts are displaced much less. Movement on the fault began in the late Oligocene as shown by coarse megabreccias southwest of the fault (Crowell, 1954b). Right slip apparently accumulated primarily from late Miocene to earliest Pleistocene, and Pleistocene dip slip took place along the fault locally (Crowell, 1950, p. 1643).

Recently Paschall and Off (1961) questioned this interpretation and have concluded that geological relations near Castaic can be explained through dip slip involving reversals of movement but without recourse to strike slip of many miles. Subsurface studies, based primarily on electric-log correlations within several oil fields and along the fault, indicate to them that Upper Miocene strata interfinger across the fault, although other geologists do not agree. According to them, the anorthosite-bearing conglomerate was eroded from basement now buried by younger sediments; they discount evidence indicating that sediments older than the conglomerate mantle the basement in the apparent source region. They interpret bodies of gabbroic and anorthositic rocks at the San Gabriel fault as segments of nearby basement floor brought to light by steep folding near the fault; the writer interprets them as fault slices within the fault zone brought in by predominant right slip of 15–20 miles. Paschall and Off feel that gneissic clasts in the Violin Breccia were derived from narrow fault slices of gneiss within the San Gabriel zone; the volume of breccia and the paucity of other clast types appear to the writer to require derivation from a far more extensive gneissic source area. They consider that the regional distribution of older sedimentary rocks, such as Paleocene and Eocene, have slip significance; here it is interpreted, but not proved, as separation only. The juxtaposition of two Mio-Pliocene marine sections is explained here by regional trace slip of several miles; however, they explain it as the result of sheltered sedimentation behind headlands with nearby open-water sedimentation on the west. The difficulty of working with major California faults is pointed up by this controversy. Even where there is a large amount of information, including a wealth of subsurface data, the interpretation is significantly different.

A comparison of the basement rocks between the Soledad and Tejon areas suggests to the writer that they have been displaced between 20 and 30 miles (Carman, 1954, p. 164; Crowell, 1960). The comparison is striking with reference to gneisses (gn_2, gn_3), including those with pink augen (ag_2, ag_3), and the presence of similar greenschists (s_2, s_3). Both regions contain granitic rocks (gr_2, gr_3) which have migmatized older gneisses, but correlation of such rocks is not yet possible. No bodies of the anorthosite-syenite complex are known in the Tejon region, although dark gneisses display textures and structures similar to those bordering the anorthosite-syenite mass of the Soledad region. Several small slices of anorthosite and related rocks in the San Gabriel fault zone northwest of Castaic, including one which perhaps provided a source for a local tongue of megabreccia in the Violin Breccia, were possibly sliced from extensions of the Soledad anorthosite. On the surface, however, the anorthosite-syenite rocks do not reach westward as far as the San Gabriel fault in the San Gabriel Mountains, so it is unlikely that with large strike slip they will be found in the Tejon region. The fault has probably cut through the terrane some distance from the anorthosite-syenite mass but has not sliced off a major part of the mass—only local extensions.

The correlation between the Soledad and Tejon regions is strengthened by the resemblance between the two suites of Oligocene rocks ($\emptyset_2$, $\emptyset_3$) (Carman, 1954, p. 86, 164). The volcanic (Fig. 6, v_2, v_3) and associated sedimentary rocks are similar, but not identical, and need further study. Units of the Miocene sequence overlying these rocks in the Tejon region contain large clasts of anorthosite and related rocks which were probably transported from the San Gabriel Mountain terrain, although possibly they were reworked from unknown, unexposed, or unpreserved pre-middle Miocene breccias. Although Eocene and Paleocene strata in both regions have not yet been adequately studied, and the original distribution of these strata is not known, Eocene beds in the Tejon region (E_3) and the Orocopia Mountains (E_1) are similar lithologically and are of the same age (Kirkpatrick, 1958). In both areas, clasts are nearly identical, and portions of the northern basin margin are preserved; further study may reveal a displaced geological "line." Eocene strata at the southern end of the San Joaquin Valley, north of the San Andreas zone, differ lithologically and lie on entirely different basement rocks.

All rocks older than Oligocene-early Miocene are displaced approximately the same amount on the combined San Andreas and San Gabriel faults. There is no compelling evidence that the San Andreas fault was active in this region before that time, although the region was tectonically active. Perhaps an east-west tectonic system, related to the Transverse Ranges and the Murray fracture zone (Menard, 1955), was active in the early Tertiary and was primarily responsible for the outlines of basins. The existence of coarse sedimentary breccias of Oligocene-early Miocene age along the Big Pine and San Gabriel faults suggests that both originated at about the same time. Other subparallel faults of the San Andreas system in southern California may have been active in the early Tertiary, and faults to the southwest of the San Gabriel fault, such as the Eocene Grade Valley fault (?), may have been the principal strands of the San Andreas system in the early Tertiary. Displacements on these faults may be one of the factors accounting for the difference between 160 and 175 miles noted as likely for post early Miocene slip, but factors, such as uncertainties in time correlations and deformation within blocks, may also be significant.

The San Gabriel fault, considered here as an integral part of the San Andreas system, no doubt meets the San Andreas fault zone at depth at its northwest end (Crowell, 1950). On the southeast, however, its course and characteristics are still incompletely known. The fault apparently bifurcates in midcourse into a southern branch which lies along the southern margin of the San Gabriel Range and a northern branch in the center of the range. The northern fault is offset by younger faults (Ehlig, 1958); the southern branch enmeshes with active faults of the Malibu-Cucamonga fault zone. Both continue into the region of Cajon Pass but apparently terminate at the active San Jacinto fault rather than continuing into the accepted San Andreas fault. In short, it is not clear how the postulated 30 miles of predominant right slip on the San Gabriel fault zone is adjusted at its eastern end.

Recently Woodford (1960) compiled data on the distribution of basement rocks in a large area of southern California which includes the San Andreas zone from Tejon Pass on the northwest to about 10 miles east of San Gorgonio Pass. The area of his map is not large enough to include rocks of the western Tejon region and the Orocopia Mountains. He grouped the basement types into eight units which apparently constitute three south-trending belts and concluded that strike-slip displacements on major faults of no more than 30 miles would adequately explain their present distribution. He ignores the San Gabriel fault but shows the San Andreas as a through-going fault in the region north of San Gorgonio Pass. He has assembled some useful information on the rock types in the region but has not described correlateable "lines" across major faults to establish slip nor discussed the possibility of regional trace slip to explain irregular separations along the San Andreas zone.

Many metamorphic units, like sedimentary ones, are tabular and flat-lying when considered on a regional scale and, therefore, may be displaced largely by trace slip. For example, widely distributed masses of greenschist (Pelona, Orocopia, etc.) by themselves are of little use at present in working out displacements on major faults. They are low grade metamorphosed sediments with included volcanic rocks and have not been studied sufficiently for correlation from body to body for reconstruction of their original area of deposition, or for finding "lines" to determine slip. An explanation of their present outcrop distribution should consider major strike slip and vertical movements which may have exposed the schist from beneath thrust movement zones as in the San Gabriel Mountains (Ehlig, 1958,) or depressed them into the subsurface. Other units of Woodford (1960), such as the upper Paleozoic limestone and related rocks, are widespread beyond his map and probably also have a gentle dip when considered on a regional scale. Metamorphic convergence (C. R. Allen, 1957a, p. 338; Schwarcz, 1960), in which rocks of different origin become similar upon metamorphism, may account for the lack of apparent offsets in some terrains. Considerable strike slip in combination with other tectonic events may be required to bring rocks of contrasting metamorphic facies and grade into juxtaposition across some major faults. At other places marked contrast in metamorphic grade and facies may be the result of dip slip only.

The hypothesis of a 160-mile, combined, right slip on the San Gabriel and San Andreas faults proposed here depends on the correlation of groups of contacts and unusual associations of rocks with complex geologic histories. Each segment of the terrane includes a cluster of contacts, steep in the basement and less steep, but not flat, in the superjacent series. Many of the contacts dip and strike in various directions and intersect to form groups of lines. The cluster of contacts and linear intersections, including many near vertical contacts, is only a few miles wide and may be considered on a regional scale as a diffuse "line" or "point" for finding slip. Many of these contact planes clearly were steep before displacement, and no combination of folding with erosion and preservation can account for their present position without major strike slip. Knowledge of rocks along the fault zone, although far from complete, is sufficient to assure that similar rocks, suggesting displacements less than 130–160 miles, are not likely to be found. The argument depends heavily upon the adequacy of correlation, and most geologists will feel that more work needs to be done before correlation is definitely established and that unequivocal displaced geological "lines" should be found. Some will feel that this preliminary hypothesis should not be promulgated until such work is completed. The procedure underway is to study intensively each rock association involved in the correlation in the area in which it is found in a broad zone along the faults (*see*, Crowell and Walker, 1962). Such studies, along with detailed studies of all rocks in small areas, should in time provide the needed data. The studies should emphasize three separate but related aspects: the petrography and stratigraphy of the rocks, the geologic history of the complete association, and the geometry of elements comprising the terrains or the search for geological "lines."

Discussion

IF MAJOR faults in California have displacements of many tens of miles, our manner of approach to geological research is affected. No single man or small group of geologists can map in detail a broad belt astride the fault that is several hundred miles long. Intensive studies of all rocks in small areas are badly needed, particularly in basement terranes, but other approaches need consideration if we are to find answers in our generation.

The geology across many major faults is unrelated so that an investigator in mapping a quadrangle, in effect, maps two distinctly different areas. Only rocks which are younger than much of the movement on the fault can be recognized on both sides. One might learn significant facts about the fault, such as the orientation of the fault surface, the character and orientation of minor structures and slices within the fault zone, and the timing of some of the movements along it, but the principal question of total displacement is unanswered. In most government and economic work the geologist's purpose is not to seek an explanation but to study a special and limited area which may or may not provide clues to the answer. Slips can be found only through a systematic search for offset counterparts—a search which may cover a very large area. In addition, conventional studies of small areas do not provide the data needed for the solution of specific problems. The practice of field geology is so difficult and there are so many things to observe that one geologist usually records data needed by another only by accident or prearrangement. In the study of geologic literature on California, semantic difficulties ever arise. In one area of basement terrane north of Los Angeles, for example, four competent geologists have recently applied four different petrographic names to the same rock complex. Only through visiting the area can another geologist acquire a mental picture of the rocks described. Although it is unfortunate that descriptive nomenclature is unsatisfactory or is ill applied by geologists, meaningful work in correlation is only possible if the rocks involved are compared by a single geologist. The literature is of use primarily in leading a geologist to areas and rocks that are likely to reveal features significant to his problem.

Other types of field studies designed to find solutions to problems are, therefore, necessary. Projects should be limited in scope so that results are obtained in a few years. Even if there are years available for investigation, certain phases should be separated from the whole and completed independently. With respect to California tectonic problems, the geology along individual faults can be studied at different scales. Small-scale maps compiled from literature or mapped by reconnaissance may reveal areas critical to understanding the fault, which then should be mapped at larger scale. Within these areas, smaller patches may provide clues to critical problems and require mapping at even larger scale. Each lithologic unit requires characterization; features which antedate the faulting, those that developed during faulting, and those that postdate it need discrimination. If long-distance correlations are suspected, each rock needs individual comparison. The study of individual faults can be limited with respect to a time-interval as well. Where sedimentary units of the same age are exposed on both sides of a fault, these can be investigated to give a synoptic picture of deformation during and since the time of deposition; basement studies may be studies of the time-interval before faulting.

Data from all such studies need to be portrayed on special maps. Paleogeographic maps are of little value unless they take into consideration the slip on major faults (Corey, 1954). Maps on which all possible geologic "lines" are assembled may aid the geometric study of faults within the San Andreas system. For some areas it is now possible to prepare paleogeologic maps showing the distribution of rock units at designated times in the past. It may even be possible to prepare some paleodynamic maps showing which faults were active and which other structures were under development for limited intervals in the past. Such a map for California, dealing with the present and showing data from seismology, geodesy, and geomorphology, would be very illuminating (Buwalda, 1952) and would emphasize the diverse types of deformations now in progress. All such studies will aid in portraying the strain history and structural evolution of the crust of California.

An ultimate goal of tectonic research is an understanding of structural mechanics. Some geologists have drawn mechanical conclusions from the pattern of all faults on a geologic map (Moody and Hill, 1956; Lensen, 1959; Williams, 1959), but such deductions are not always sound. Some faults are younger than others, some have moved in different ways at different times, some are dead, some are still active, most have unknown slips, and on many the dip at depth is uncertain. Some dead faults have been rotated or folded by later deformation. Although limited sound conclusions can perhaps be drawn for a single synoptic sample, we need maps showing strain history. With a kinematic view of the structural evolution in hand, some dynamic conclusions may then be warranted.

Viewpoints on mechanics play an important role in the controversy in California on the significance of major strike-slip faulting. Many geologists feel instinctively that dip slip should be assumed on all faults until there is incontrovertible evidence that strike slip has occurred. Others, perhaps also following the guiding principle that an explanation involving the least expenditure of energy is apt to be the correct one, will admit to a little strike slip, although less energy may be required for major strike slip than for major dip slip. Others accede to 30 miles only as reasonable. It appears that at present there is enough evidence in hand, from California as well as from many other regions, to make such instinctive judgments untenable. All conclusions and feelings with regard to slip should await a diligent search for displaced counterparts. On the other hand, it is wise to maintain a conservative view toward alleged correlations and to insist on the assembly of a large body of pertinent data before passing judgment. The crux of the matter is essentially whether the correlation of geologic "lines" is sound and to refrain from any mechanical conclusions until data on correlations are marshalled.

Conservatism in mechanics can also take an entirely different guise. Hill and Dibblee (1953, p. 450) appeal to the principle of uniformitarianism and consider it more reasonable mechanically for intermittent movements on faults to have followed the same direction in the past as at present. Because many of the major faults displayed strike-slip offsets during modern earthquakes and seismic and geodetic data indicate predominant strike slip, in searching for evidences of slip in the past record, geologists should look for strike-slip offsets. Many believe that mechanically it is more reasonable to expect forces to maintain approximately the same orientation for long times than for the orientation of forces to change drastically and unsystematically, first giving rise to vertical movements (perhaps even with reversals) and ending with strike slip. Despite the reasonableness of this viewpoint, which may provide the basis for a preliminary hypothesis, eventual understanding again lies in painstaking reconstruction of the movement picture of strain in crustal rocks through time—that is, in reconstructing the kinematics. But some faults, such as the San Gabriel fault along its northern part, move with one kind of slip for a long period and then move in another sense later (Crowell, 1950, p. 1643; Crowell, 1952a). Perhaps these different strains, which occurred on the same fault at different times, arose in inhomogeneous near-surface rocks with similar fundamental force at depth, but this explanation is at present hypothetical.

Along the major California faults, virtually no attention has yet been paid to the patterns of joints and minor faults nor to the orientation of minor structures within fault zones. Minor folds have been noted at places, but primarily the major fault zones are unexposed and lie beneath alluvium in a topographic furrow. Where the zones are exposed, however, the fault rocks need careful investigation. In the few good exposures the zones of active faults display masses of greenish and black gouge and comminuted rock, locally altered hydrothermally, which have been described petrographically in only rare instances (Waters and Campbell, 1935; Hsu, 1955). At places the shape and orientation of phacoids and rare minor structures suggest upward squeezing and appear to be the result of local upward relief of stress rather than to fundamental movements at depth. Mylonites along the San Andreas are relatively rare and, where found, commonly occur within fault-bounded slices. They appear to be primarily the result of movements at depth, older than Recent, either within the major fault zone or in country rock transected by it and, therefore, perhaps not at all related to it (Hsu, 1955).

In summary, difficulties and concepts of correlation need emphasis, for in the end it is the acceptability of long distance correlations upon which the determination of strike slip of many miles depends. In addition to assembling an impressive amount of data to establish sound correlations, it is necessary to find suitable explanations for all geologic relationships between correlated "lines." Many pitfalls ensue from dealing with parts and thinking in terms of the whole. For this reason basement rocks cannot be ignored. In addition, since faults displace rocks whose properties should be dealt with in total, it may be erroneous to consider only one or a few of their many characterizing features, such as their electrical or magnetic properties. Offsets, or the lack of them, based on correlations of electric-log units, biostratigraphic units, or time stratigraphic units (Paschall and Off, 1961), are not only concerned with mere separations instead of slips, but with only one characterizing aspect of the rocks as well. For example, isopachs of biostratigraphic units may cross a fault with no apparent offset, whereas, the lithology may be significantly different, and the fault may possess considerable slip. Moreover, single characteristics may find chance counterparts on the opposite sides of a fault, but conclusive correlation cannot be established until the entire body of geologic data has been appraised.

Conclusions

ALTHOUGH it is premature to draw conclusions about the significance of strike-slip movements of hundreds of miles on the major faults in California, the evidence in hand suggests that 160–175 miles of right slip on the San Andreas and closely associated faults since early Miocene is probable. In both central and southern California, independent matches of offset terrains, displaced approximately 160–175 miles, have been described briefly, but the assembling of convincing data to establish the correlations remains. Several younger and lesser displacements have been described, some of which are quite convincing because they are geometrically sound and are concerned with slip and not with separation alone.

Displacements greater than 160 miles referred to in the geological literature depend on evidence and arguments of a different order of acceptability, although in time some or all of them may turn out to be correct. Cretaceous and Eocene strata exhibit possible separations of more than 320 and 220 miles, respectively, but the original distribution of these low dipping units, when pictured on a regional scale, has not yet been reconstructed, and offset geological "lines" have not been described. Older and greater displacements, up to as much as 400 miles, depend on a supposed alignment in the past of the batholithic cores of the Sierra Nevada, Coast, and Peninsular ranges, and also on the alignment of the boundary between Sierran basement on the east and Franciscan rocks on the west. Much more work needs to be done to make these proposed correlations acceptable.

There is no compelling evidence that faults of the San Andreas system are older than early Tertiary. Some faults were apparently first active in the Eocene and others in the Oligocene. In southern California the total displacement on the combined San Gabriel and

San Andreas faults was probably acquired since earliest Miocene, because all rocks older than this appear to be displaced the same amount. The rate of movement implied for this 160 miles in about 25 million years (Durham, Jahns, and Savage, 1954, fig. 2; Evernden, Kistler, and Curtis, 1959; Holmes, 1960, p. 204; Kulp, 1961, p. 1111) is about 0.4 inches per year (3⅓ feet or a meter per century). This rate is significantly less than the present drift of the coastal region of more than 2 inches per year (Whitten, 1955, p. 75). It is invalid to assume a constant rate for such a long time and over such a long stretch of the fault system, but it is of interest that this average rate is much less than that measured in active areas at present. In the past first one part and then another of a fault in the system has acquired displacement. Slips along individual faults differ markedly from place to place—younger rocks were displaced less than older; opposing blocks across faults were deformed differently at different times; and faults within the system (either subparallel or converging with others) were alternately major or minor elements in the system.

Data from belts along major faults need geometric analysis and a systematic search for offset geological "lines." Sedimentary units that have a low dip on a regional scale in particular require intensive study from this viewpoint, and the possibility of regional trace slip of flat-lying formations needs more widespread recognition. Units that were laid down during limited time intervals need attention, for they may give clues to deformation during and since that interval. Basement terranes hold the ultimate key to both prefaulting histories and total slip and should be especially studied by isotopic dating, as well as by geological methods. Suspected correlations, both short and long distant and implying any magnitude and orientation of slip, need detailed investigation. Enough data now indicate the likelihood of large strike slip so that field tests of the hypothesis should be designed. We need diligent searches for diagnostic features to find slips of any magnitude unequivocally, and the consequences of slip of many miles need analysis. In a few years such studies may lead to understanding the nature and history of the San Andreas system.

References Cited

Unpublished theses are listed with References Cited as a convenience to the reader.

ALF, R. M., 1948, A mylonite belt in the southeastern San Gabriel Mountains, California: Geol. Soc. America Bull., v. 59, p. 1101–1120

ALLEN, C. R., 1957a, San Andreas fault zone in San Gorgonio Pass, southern California: Geol. Soc. America Bull., v. 68, p. 315–350

— 1957b, The San Andreas fault: its significance in California's past and future: Eng. and Sci. Monthly, v. 20, p. 17–21

ALLEN, C. R., SILVER, L. T., AND STEHLI, F. G., 1960, Agua Blanca fault—a major transverse structure of northern Baja California, Mexico: Geol. Soc. America Bull., v. 71, p. 457–482

ALLEN, J. E., 1946, Geology of the San Juan Bautista quadrangle, California: Calif. Div. Mines Bull. 133, 112 p.

ANDERSON, E. M., 1951, The dynamics of faulting and dyke formation with applications to Britain: 2nd ed., Edinburgh and London, Oliver and Boyd, 206 p.

BAILEY, E. H., 1961, Metamorphic facies of the Franciscan formation of California and their geologic significance (Abstract): Geol. Soc. America Special Paper 68, p. 4–5

BAILEY, T. L., AND JAHNS, R. H., Geology of the Transverse Range province, southern California: Calif. Div. Mines Bull. 170, chap. 2, p. 83–106

BECKWITH, R. H., 1941, Trace-slip faults: Am. Assoc. Petroleum Geologists Bull., v. 25, p. 2181–2193

BUWALDA, J. P., 1952, Diverse but simultaneous orogeny (Abstract): Geol. Soc. America Bull., v. 63, p. 1322–1323

CAREY, S. W., 1958, A tectonic approach to continental drift, p. 177–355, in continental drift: a symposium: Hobart, Australia, Univ. Tasmania, Geology Dept., 375 p.

CARMAN, MAX F., JR., 1954, Geology of the Lockwood Valley area, Kern and Ventura counties, California: Unpub. Ph.D. thesis, Univ. Calif., Los Angeles, 194 p.

CLARK, B. L., 1930, Tectonics of the Coast Ranges of Middle California: Geol. Soc. America Bull., v. 41, p. 747–828

CLARK, L. D., 1960, Foothills fault system, western Sierra Nevada, California: Geol. Soc. America Bull., v. 71, p. 483–496

COREY, W. H., 1954, Tertiary basins of southern California: Calif. Div. Mines Bull. 170, chap. 3, p. 73–83

CROWELL, J. C., 1950, Geology of Hungry Valley area, southern California: Am. Assoc. Petroleum Geologists Bull., v. 34, p. 1623–1646

— 1952a, Probable large lateral displacement on the San Gabriel fault, southern California: Am. Assoc. Petroleum Geologists Bull., v. 36, p. 2026–2035

— 1952b, Geology of the Lebec quadrangle, California: Calif. Div. Mines Special Rept. 24, 23 p.

— 1954a, Geology of the Ridge basin area, Los Angeles and Ventura counties, California: Calif. Div. Mines Bull. 170, map sheet 7

— 1954b, Strike-slip displacement of the San Gabriel fault, southern California: Calif. Div. Mines Bull. 170, chap. 4, p. 49–52

— 1955, Violin breccia in Transverse Ranges, California (Abstract): Geol. Soc. America Bull., v. 66, p. 1546

— 1959, Problems of fault nomenclature: Am. Assoc. Petroleum Geologists Bull., v. 43, p. 2653–2674

— 1960, The San Andreas fault in southern California: Copenhagen, Internat. Cong. Rept. 21, pt. 18, p. 45–52

CROWELL, J. C., AND SUSUKI, T., 1959, Eocene stratigraphy and paleontology, Orocopia Mountains, southeastern California: Geol. Soc. America Bull., v. 70, p. 581–592

CROWELL, J. C., AND WALKER, J. W. R., 1962, Anorthosite and related rocks along the San Andreas fault, southern California: Univ. Calif. Pub. Geol. Sci., v. 40, no. 4 (in press)

CURTIS, G. H., EVERNDEN, J. F., AND LIPSON, J., 1958, Age determination of some granitic rocks in California by the potassium-argon method: Calif. Div. Mines Special Rept. 54, 16 p.

DERLETH, CHARLES, JR., 1907, The destructive extent of the California earthquake of 1906, p. 79–212 in Jordan, D. S., Editor, The California earthquake of 1906: San Francisco, A. M. Robertson, 371 p.

DIBBLEE, T. W., JR., 1952, Geology of the Saltdale quadrangle, California: Calif. Div. Mines Bull. 160, 66 p.

— 1954, Geology of the Imperial Valley region, California: Calif. Div. Mines Bull. 170, chap. 2, p. 21–28

— 1960a, Geology of the Rogers Lake and Kramer quadrangles, California: U. S. Geol. Survey Bull. 1089-B, 139 p.

— 1960b, Geologic map of the Lancaster quadrangle, Los Angeles County, California: U. S. Geol. Survey Mineral Inv. Field Studies Map MF-76

— 1961, Geologic map of the Bouquet Reservoir quadrangle, Los Angeles County, California: U. S. Geol. Survey Mineral Inv. Field Studies Map MF-79

DURHAM, J. W., AND KIRK, M. V., 1950, Age of the Coraliochama beds of the Pacific Coast (Abstract): Geol. Soc. America Bull., v. 61, p. 1537

DURHAM, J. W., JAHNS, R. H., AND SAVAGE, D. E., 1954, Marine-nonmarine relationships in the Cenozoic section of California: Calif. Div. Mines Bull. 170, chap. 3, p. 59–71

EHLIG, PERRY, L. 1958, Geology of the Mount Baldy region of the San Gabriel Mountains, California: Unpub. Ph.D. thesis, Univ. Calif., Los Angeles, 153 p.

EVERNDEN, J. F., Kistler, R., AND CURTIS, G. H., 1959, Cenozoic time scale of the west coast (Abstract): Geol. Soc. America Bull., v. 70, p. 1718

FAIRBANKS, H. W., 1894, Geology of northern Ventura, Santa Barbara, San Luis Obispo, Monterey, and San Benito counties: Calif. State Min. Bur., 12th Ann. Rept. of State Mineralogist, p. 493–526

— 1907, The great earthquake rift of California, p. 319–338 *in* Jordan, D. S., *Editor*, The California earthquake of 1906: San Francisco, A. M. Robertson, 371 p.

FISHER, R. V., AND DIBBLEE, T. W., JR., 1961, Geology and possible tectonic significance of Munson Creek fault, San Rafael Mountains, California: Am. Assoc. Petroleum Geologists Bull., v. 45, p. 1572–1581

GIBSON, W. M., 1961, Geodimeter measurements across the San Andreas fault, California (Abstract): Geol. Soc. America Spec. Paper 68, p. 27

GILLULY, J., 1949, Distribution of mountain building in geologic time: Geol. Soc. America Bull., v. 60, p. 561–590

HALL, C. A., JR., 1960, Displaced Miocene molluscan provinces along the San Andreas fault, California: Univ. Calif. Pubs. Geol. Sci., v. 34, p. 281–308

HAMILTON, W. B., 1961, Origin of Gulf of California: Geol. Soc. America Bull., v. 72, p. 1307–1318

HARTMAN, DONALD C., 1957, Geology of the Upper Wagon Road Canyon area, southern California: Unpub. M. A. thesis, Univ. Calif., Los Angeles, 95 p.

HAYS, WILLIAM H., 1957, Geology of part of the Cottonwood Springs quadrangle, Riverside County, California: Unpub. Ph.D. thesis, Yale Univ., 324 p.

HESS, F. L., 1910, Gold mining in the Randsburg quadrangle, California: U. S. Geol. Survey Bull. 430, p. 23–47

HEWETT, D. F., 1954, A fault map of the Mojave Desert region: Calif. Div. Mines Bull. 170, chap. 4, p. 15–18

HIGGINS, C. G., 1961, San Andreas fault north of San Francisco, California: Geol. Soc. America Bull., v. 72, p. 51–68

HIGGS, D. V., 1954, Anorthosite and related rocks of the western San Gabriel Mountains, southern California: Univ. Calif. Pubs. Geol. Sci., v. 30, p. 171–222

HILL, M. L., 1947, Classification of faults: Am. Assoc. Petroleum Geologists Bull., v. 31, p. 1669–73

— 1959, Dual classification of faults: Am. Assoc. Petroleum Geologists Bull., v. 43, p. 217–21

HILL, M. L., AND DIBBLEE, T. W., JR., 1953, San Andreas, Garlock and Big Pine faults, California: Geol. Soc. America Bull., v. 64, p. 443–458

HOLMES, ARTHUR, 1960, A revised geological time-scale: Edinburgh Geol. Soc. Trans., v. 17, p. 183–216

HULIN, C. D., 1925, Geology and ore deposits of the Randsburg quadrangle, California: Calif. Div. Mines Bull. 95, 152 p.

HURLEY, R. J., 1960, New evidence on the northward continuation of the San Andreas fault (Abstract): Geol. Soc. America Bull., v. 71, p. 1894

HSU, K. J., 1955, Granulites and mylonites of the region about Cucamonga and San Antonio Canyons, San Gabriel Mountains, California: Univ. Calif. Pubs. Geol. Sci., v. 30, p. 223–352

IRWIN, W. P., 1960, Geologic reconnaissance of the northern Coast Ranges and Klamath Mountains, California: Calif. Div. Mines Bull. 179, 80 p.

JAHNS, R. H., 1954, Geology of the Peninsular Range province, southern California: Calif. Div. Mines Bull. 170, chap. 2, p. 29–52

JAHNS, R. H., AND MUEHLBERGER, W. R., 1954, Geology of the Soledad basin, Los Angeles County, California: Calif. Div. Mines Bull. 170, map sheet 6

JENKINS, O. P., 1943, Geologic formations and economic development of the oil and gas fields of California: Calif. Div. Mines Bull. 118, 773 p.

JENNINGS, C. W., 1958, San Luis Obispo sheet, geologic map of California: Calif. Div. Mines

JENNINGS, C. W., AND STRAND, R. G., 1958, Santa Cruz sheet, geologic map of California: Calif. Div. Mines

JOHNSON, BRADFORD K., 1952, Geology of the Castaic Creek-Elizabeth Lake Canyon area Los Angeles County, California: Unpub. M. A. thesis, Univ. Calif., Los Angeles, 44 p.

JORDAN, D. S., 1907, The earthquake rift of April, 1906, p. 1-62. in Jordan, D. S., Editor, The California earthquake of 1906: San Francisco, A. M. Robertson, 371 p.

KELLEY, V. C., 1960, Slips and separations: Geol. Soc. America Bull., v. 71, p. 1545-1546

KENNEDY, W. Q., 1945, The Great Glen fault: Geol. Soc. London Quart. Jour., v. 102, p. 41-76

KIESSLING, EDMUND, 1958, Geology of the southwest portion of the Lockwood Valley quadrangle, Ventura County, California: Unpub. M. A. thesis, Univ. Calif., Los Angeles, 117 p.

KING, P. B., 1958, Evolution of modern surface features of western North America, p. 3-60 in Hubbs, C. L., Editor, Zoogeography: Am. Assoc. Advancement of Sci., 509 p.

— 1959, The evolution of North America: Princeton, New Jersey, Princeton Univ. Press, 189 p.

KIRKPATRICK, JOHN C., 1958, A study of some marine middle Eocene formations in southern California: Unpub. M. A. thesis, Univ. Calif., Los Angeles, 75 p.

KULP, J. L., 1961, Geologic time scale: Science, v. 133, p. 1105-1114

KUNDERT, C. J., 1955, Los Angeles sheet, geologic map of California: Calif. Div. Mines

LAMAR, DONALD L., 1961, Structural evolution of the northern margin of the Los Angeles basin: Unpub. Ph.D. thesis, Univ. Calif., Los Angeles, 142 p.

LAWSON, A. C., 1893, The post-Pliocene diastrophism of the coast of southern California: Univ. Calif. Pubs. Geol. Sci., v. 1, p. 115-160

— 1895, Sketch of the geology of the San Francisco Peninsula: U. S. Geol. Survey, 15th Ann. Rept., p. 405-476

LAWSON, A. C., AND OTHERS, 1908, The California earthquake of April 18, 1906: Carnegie Inst. Washington, v. 1, pt. 1, 254 p.; atlas, 82 p.

LENSEN, G. J., 1959, Secondary faulting and transcurrent splay-faulting at transcurrent fault intersections: New Zealand Jour. Geology and Geophy., v. 2, p. 729-734

MASON, R. G., 1958, A magnetic survey off the west coast of the United States between latitudes 32° and 36° N., longitudes 121° and 128° W.: Geophys. Jour., v. 1, p. 320-329

MASON, R. G., AND RAFF, A. D., 1961, Magnetic survey off the west coast of North America, 40° N. latitude to 42° N. latitude: Geol. Soc. America Bull., v. 72, p. 1259–1266

MENARD, H. W., 1955, Deformation of the northeastern Pacific Basin and the west coast of North America: Geol. Soc. America Bull., v. 66, p. 1149–1198

— 1960, The East Pacific Rise: Science, v. 132, p. 1737–1746

MILLER, W. J., 1940, Some features of faulting in southern California: Jour. Geology, v. 48, p. 385–420

— 1944, Geology of the Palm Springs-Blythe strip, Riverside County, California: California Jour. Mines and Geology, v. 40, p. 11–72

MOODY, J. D., AND HILL, M. J., 1956, Wrench-fault tectonics: Geol. Soc. America Bull., v. 67, p. 1207–1246

MOORE, J. G., 1959, The quartz diorite boundary line in the western United States: Jour. Geology, v. 67, p. 198–210

MUEHLBERGER, W. R., 1954, Geology of the Quail Mountains, San Bernandino County: Calif. Div. Mines Bull. 170, map sheet 16

— 1958, Geology of northern Soledad Basin, Los Angeles County, California: Am. Assoc. Petroleum Geologists Bull., v. 42, p. 1812–1844

MUEHLBERGER, W. R., AND HILL, H. S., 1958, Geology of the central Sierra Pelona, Los Angeles County, California: Am. Jour. Sci., v. 256, p. 630–643

NEUERBURG, G. J., AND GOTTFRIED, D., 1954, Age determinations of the San Gabriel anorthosite massif, California: Geol. Soc. America Bull., v. 65, p. 465–466

NOBLE, L. F., 1926, The San Andreas rift and some other active faults in the desert region of southeastern California: Carnegie Inst. Washington Year Book 25, p. 415–428

— 1932, Excursion to the San Andreas fault and Cajon Pass: Washington, 16th Internat. Geol. Cong. Guidebook 15, p. 10–20

— 1953, Geology of the Pearland quadrangle, California: U. S. Geol. Survey Geol, Quadrangle Map GQ 24

— 1954a, Geology of the Valyermo quadrangle and vicinity, California: U. S. Geol. Survey Geol, Quadrangle Map GQ 50

— 1954b, The San Andreas fault zone from Soledad Pass to Cajon Pass, California: Calif. Div. Mines Bull., 170, chap. 4, p. 37–48

NOBLE, L. F., AND WRIGHT, L. A., 1954, Geology of the central and southern Death Valley region, California: Calif. Div. Mines Bull. 170, chap. 2, p. 143–160

OAKESHOTT, G. B., 1958, Geology and Mineral deposits of the San Fernando quadrangle, Los Angeles County, California: Calif. Div. Mines Bull. 172, 147 p.

— 1959, San Andreas fault in Marin and San Mateo Counties: p. 7–24 in Oakeshott, G. B., Editor, San Francisco earthquakes of March 1957: Calif. Div. Mines Special Rept. 57, 127 p.

PASCHALL, R. H., AND OFF, T., 1961, Dip-slip versus strike-slip movement on San Gabriel fault, southern California: Am. Assoc. Petroleum Geologists Bull., v. 45, 1941–1956

PERRY, E. L., 1935, Flaws and tear faults: Am. Jour. Sci., v. 229, p. 112–124

POYNOR, WILLIAM D., 1960, Geology of the San Guillermo area and its regional correlation, Ventura County, California: Unpub. M. A. thesis, Univ. Calif., Los Angeles, 119 p.

RAFF, A. D., AND MASON, R. G., 1961, Magnetic survey off the west coast of North America, 40° N. latitude to 52° N. latitude: Geol. Soc. America Bull., v. 72, p. 1267–1270

REED, R. D., 1933, Geology of California: Tulsa, Oklahoma, Am. Assoc. Petroleum Geologists, 355 p.

REED, R. D., AND HOLLISTER, J. S., 1936, Structural evolution of southern California: Tulsa, Oklahoma, Am. Assoc. Petroleum Geologists, 157 p.

REID, H. F., DAVIS, W. M., LAWSON, A. C., AND RANSOME, F. L., 1913, Report of the committee on the nomenclature of faults: Geol. Soc. America Bull., v. 24, p. 163–186

SCHLEE, J. S., 1952, Geology of the Mutau Flat area, Ventura County, California: Unpub. M. A. thesis, Univ. Calif., Los Angeles, 108 p.

SCHUYLER, J. D., 1897, Reservoirs for irrigation: U. S. Geol. Survey 18th Ann. Rept. pt. 4, p. 711–713

SCHWADE, I. T., CARLSON, S. A., AND O'FLYNN, J. B., 1958, Geologic environment of Cuyama Valley oil fields, California: p. 78–98 in Weeks, L. G., Editor, Habitat of Oil, Tulsa, Oklahoma, Am. Assoc. Petroleum Geologists, 1384 p.

SCHWARCZ, H. P., 1960, Sedimentation and regional metamorphism prior to intrusion of the southern California batholith (Abstract): Geol. Soc. America Bull., v. 71, p. 1969

SHARP, R. P., 1954, Physiographic features of faulting in southern California: Calif. Div. Mines Bull. 170, chap. 5, p. 21–28

SHEPARD, F. P., 1957, Northward continuation of the San Andreas rift: Seismological Soc. America Bull., v. 47, p. 263–266

SILVER, L. T., McKINNEY, C. R., DEUTSCH, S., AND BOLINGER, J., 1960, Precambrian age determinations of some crystalline rocks of the San Gabriel Mountains of southern California (Abstract): Jour. Geophys. Res., v. 65, p. 2522–2523

SMITH, D. D., 1959, Pleistocene offset along the San Andreas fault system of the San Francisco Peninsula, California (Abstract): Geol. Soc. America Bull., v. 70, p. 1677

SMITH, G. I., 1960, Time of the last displacement on the middle part of the Garlock fault, California: U. S. Geol. Survey Prof. Paper 400-B, p. B280

— 1962, Large lateral displacement on the Garlock fault, California, as measured from offset dike swarm: Am. Assoc. Petroleum Geologists Bull., v. 46, p. 85–104

SOLLAS, H. B. C., 1904, The face of the earth: (Translation of Suess, E. 1885, Das Antlitz der Erde), Oxford, Clarendon Press, v. 1, 604 p.

STEINBRUGGE, K. V., AND ZACHER, E. G., 1960, Creep on the San Andreas fault: Fault creep and property damage: Seismol. Soc. America Bull., v. 50, p. 389–395

TABER, S., 1907, Local effects of the California earthquake of 1906, p. 257–280 in Jordan, D. S., Editor, The California earthquake of 1906, San Francisco, A. M. Robertson, 371 p.

TALIAFERRO, N. L., 1941, Geologic history and structure of the central Coast Ranges of California: Calif. Div. Mines Bull. 118, p. 119–163

— 1942, Geologic history and correlation of the Jurassic of southwestern Oregon and California: Geol. Soc. America Bull., v. 53, p. 71–112

— 1943, The Franciscan-Knoxville problem, California: Am. Assoc. Petroleum Geologists Bull., v. 27, p. 109–219

— 1948, Geologic map of the Hollister quadrangle, California: Calif. Div. Mines Bull. 143, pl. 1.

— 1951, Geology of the San Francisco Bay counties: Calif. Div. Mines Bull. 154, p. 117–150

TOCHER, D., 1956, Earthquakes off the North Pacific Coast of the United States: Seismol. Soc. America Bull., v. 46, p. 165–173

— 1960, Creep on the San Andreas fault: Creep rate and related measurements at Vineyard, California: Seismol. Soc. America Bull., v. 50, p. 396–403

VACQUIER, V., 1959, Measurement of horizontal displacement along faults in the ocean floor: Nature, v. 183, p. 452–453

VACQUIER, V., RAFF, A. D., AND WARREN, R. E., 1961, Horizontal displacements in the floor of the northeastern Pacific Ocean: Geol. Soc. America Bull., v. 72, p. 1251–1258

VICKERY, F. P., 1925, The structural dynamics of the Livermore region: Jour. Geology, v. 33, p. 608–628

WALLACE, R. E., 1949, Structure of a portion of the San Andreas rift in southern California: Geol. Soc. America Bull., v. 60, p. 781–806

WARE, GLEN C., JR., 1958, The geology of a portion of the Mecca Hills, Riverside County, California: Unpub. M. A. thesis, Univ. Calif., Los Angeles, 60 p.

WATERS, A. C., AND CAMPBELL, C. D., 1935, Mylonites from the San Andreas fault zone: Am. Jour. Sci., v. 229, p. 473–503

WHITTEN, C. A., 1955, Measurements of earth movements in California: Calif. Div. Mines Bull. 171, p. 75–80

WHITTEN, C. A., AND CLAIRE, C. N., 1960, Creep on the San Andreas fault: Analysis of geodetic measurements along the San Andreas fault: Seismol. Soc. America Bull., v. 50, p. 404–416

WEISE, J. H., 1950, Geology and mineral resources of the Neenach quadrangle, California: Calif. Div. Mines Bull. 153, 53 p.

WILLIAMS, A., 1959, A structural history of the Girvan district, southwest Ayrshire: Roy. Soc. Edinburgh Trans., v. 63, pt. 3, p. 629–667

WILLIS, B., 1938, San Andreas rift, California: Jour. Geology, v. 46, p. 793–827; 1017–1057

WILLIS, R., 1925, Physiography of the California Coast Ranges: Geol. Soc. America Bull., v. 36, p. 641–678

WILSON, I. F., 1943, Geology of the San Benito quadrangle, California: Calif. Jour. Mines and Geology, v. 39, p. 183–270

WINTERER, E. L., AND DURHAM, D. L., 1958, Geologic map of a part of the Ventura Basin, Los Angeles County, California: U. S. Geol. Survey Oil and Gas Inv. Map OM 196

WOODFORD, A. O., 1960, Bedrock patterns and strike-slip faulting in southwestern California: Am. Jour. Sci., v. 258-A, p. 400–417

ZIONY, JOSEPH I., 1958, Geology of the Abel Mountain area, Kern and Ventura counties, California: Unpub. M. A. thesis, Univ. Calif., Los Angeles, 99 p.

Manuscript Received by the Secretary of the Society, June 20, 1960

Index*

Analysis of faults, geometric, 12, 50
Anaverde Formation, 18
Ancient fault zones, 43
  Mesozoic fault zones, 24
Antelope Valley, 6
Approach to geological research, 44, 45

Banning fault, 5
Bazeley, W. J. M., 20
Bear Valley fault, 6, 10
Big Pine fault, 4, 32, **34**, 35, 42
  Alignment with Garlock fault, 35
Branner, John C., 8

Cajon Pass, 6, 10, 20, 42
Calaveras fault, 6
Cape Mendocino, 5
Castaic, 40, 41
Castaic Formation, 31
Clearwater fault, 32
Clemens Well fault, 28
Coachella Valley, 6, 7
Continent-ocean contact, 24

Death Valley fault zone, 33

Elsinore fault, 6

Fault
  landforms, 7
    flank-fan depressions, 7
    offset streams, 7, 17
    sag ponds, 7
    sags, 7
    scarps, 7
    shutter ridges, 7
    slice ridges, 7
    topographic expression, 6
  movement, rate of, 50
  nomenclature, 3, 4
  rocks, 48
    gouge, 48
    hydrothermal alteration, 48
  scarps, 7
  system, 4
  zone, 3
    ancient, 43
    Death Valley, 33

interpretation of, 10
  Malibu-Cucamonga, 35, 42
  Mesozoic, 24
  San Andreas, 3, 5, 6, 10
Faults
  recurrent movement on, 9, 17, 46
  topographic expression of, 6, 7
  total displacements on, 16
Faults, major
  Banning, 5
  Bear Valley, 6, 10
  Big Pine, 4, 32, 34, 35, 42
  Calaveras, 6
  Clearwater, 32
  Clemens Well, 28
  Death Valley, 33
  Elsinore, 6
  Garlock, 4, 8, 11, 25, 32, **33,** 34
  Grade Valley, 42
  Hayward, 4, 6
  Liebre, 25, 32
  Main Coast Range, 8
  Malibu-Cucamonga, 35, 42
  Mission Creek, 5
  Nacimiento, 23
  Pilarcitos, 5, 6, 21
  Portolá-Tomales, 8
  Punchbowl, 20
  San Andreas, 3, 6
  San Gabriel, 4, 6, 13, 25, 27, 31, 32, **36,**
    39, 42
  San Jacinto, 4, 5, 6, 42
  Stevens Creek, 8
  Whittier, 35
Flaw, 4
Fletcher, G. L., 19
Fort Ross, 21, 22, 23
Fracture zones, oceanic, 24, 42
Franciscan Group, 6, 9, 21, **22,** 23, 24
Franciscan-Sierran contact, 21, **22,** 23, 24
Frazier Mountain thrust, 32

Gabilan Range, 12, 20, 25
Garlock fault, 4, 8, 11, 25, 32, **33,** 34
  Alignment with Big Pine fault, 35
Geological "lines," 12, 14, 15
Geometrical analysis of faults, 12, 50
Goler Formation, 33
Gouge, 48
Grade Valley fault, 42

---

* **Boldface** type indicates pages of principal
    treatment.